Modern Data Modes

a guide to using WSJT-X, JTDX, Fldigi, FT8, FT4, PSK, JS8, VarAC and other modes

Edited by
Steve Telenius-Lowe, PJ4DX

Radio Society of Great Britain

Published by the Radio Society of Great Britain, 3 Abbey Court, Fraser Road, Priory Business Park, Bedford MK44 3WH. Tel: 01234 832700. Web: www.rsgb.org

Published 2023.

Reprinted Digitally 2024 onwards

ISBN: 9781 9139 9533 1

Main text by Rob Walker, G3ZJQ
Additional text by Steve Telenius-Lowe, PJ4DX, and Mike Richards, G4WNC
Editing, design and layout: Steve Telenius-Lowe, PJ4DX
Cover design: Kevin Williams, M6CYB
Production: Mark Allgar, M1MPA

Printed in Great Britain by 4Edge Ltd. of Hockley, Essex

Publisher's Notes:
The opinions expressed in this book are those of the author(s) and are not necessarily those of the Radio Society of Great Britain. Whilst the information presented is believed to be correct, the publishers and their agents cannot accept responsibility for consequences arising from any inaccuracies or omissions.

This book is based on the *radiotoday Guide to HF Data on FT8 & PSK using WSJT-X and Fldigi* by Rob Walker, G3ZJQ, which was first published in 2019. It has been brought up to date for 2023 with additional sections on FT4, originally intended for high-speed contest operation, alternative weak-signal mode software programs including JTDX and MSHV, and the new keyboard-to-keyboard mode VarAC. The URL links listed in the book were all correct at the time of going to press.

Contents

About the Authors

Rob Walker, G3ZJQ

Rob wrote the *RadioToday Guide to HF Data on FT8 & PSK Using WSJT-X and Fldigi* upon which this book is based. Most of the material in the present book was written by Rob.

Rob became interested in radio and electronics construction at a very early age. He studied physics at Imperial College, London University, and graduated in 1972. He went on to do a doctorate in theoretical solid state physics at Sussex University and now boasts BA, BSc, MBA, DPhil, FIET, CEng, ARCS after his name!

After working in the commercial sector Rob became a consulting engineer and project manager. As part of this role he gained an MBA by studying at the Open University. He complemented his consultancy work with teaching at the OU as an Associate Lecturer. Currently, he is engaged as an MSc Supervisor in the Faculty of Mathematics, Computing and Technology at the Open University.

Throughout all this time Rob has remained an active radio amateur with interests spanning HF through to UHF.

Mike Richards, G4WNC

Mike provided the section covering the new VarAC mode in Chapter 4. Helped and inspired by his father, Mike took to radio and electronics at an early age and spent most of his teens building radios and guitar amplifiers. After leaving school, Mike enjoyed a successful and varied 42-year career with BT, working in a wide range of engineering specialisms. Originally licensed as G8HHA and a keen constructor, Mike became disillusioned with amateur radio as many turned to commercial equipment. His interest was revitalised in the 1970s when the Compukit UK101 computer became available. This led to experiments using radio data links to connect computers. Mike followed this up by obtaining his full licence as G4WNC, where he has maintained a strong interest in all digital modes. Mike's writing career started about 25 years ago when he took over *PW* magazine's RTTY contribution from Ron Ham. Since then, Mike has contributed several regular columns, multiple equipment reviews and several books.

Steve Telenius-Lowe, PJ4DX

Steve edited this book based on Rob's text, bringing it up to date for 2023 and looking after the design and layout of the book. Steve also wrote the additional text covering FT4, JTDX and MSHV.

Originally licensed as G8FEO while still at school, and later as G4JVG, Steve had a varied career working for the BBC followed by a three-year stint with the Post and Telecommunication Corporation of Papua New Guinea. Returning to the UK, he worked on *RadCom*, *D-i-Y Radio* and *Radio Today* at the RSGB, culminating as Managing Editor of *RadCom*. He took early retirement in 2005 and moved to the Far East, followed in 2013 by another move, this time to Bonaire in the Dutch Caribbean. He has made over 120,000 QSOs as PJ4DX and is currently active on all bands from 1.8 to 50MHz using FT8, FT4, SSB and CW.

1. Introduction

Amateur radio continues to develop over the years from its beginnings in the early 20th century to the present. Each time a new activity is spawned there are those who embrace it and those who deem it not in the 'spirit' of the hobby, and oppose its creation. Perhaps the biggest change in recent times has been the rise of the internet as both an information resource and a communications medium, but it is not the only influence digital technologies have had upon our hobby. Digital communication technologies are all around us from the PC to the tablet and mobile phone. Today, they are our constant companions. From this milieu have risen the digital modes that this book is all about.

You could argue that the first digital mode was CW using Morse code and a straight key. After all, it is an on-off modulation method: early CW transmitters used to key the PA directly. However, Morse code is a human-readable system of communications that relies upon highly skilled operators. It is not what is meant today by a digital mode. Radio Teletype (RTTY) was one of the earliest 'true' digital modes but it relied upon mechanical teletype machines that were both large and noisy to operate. Today digital modes are intimately tied to computer technology and software. They can be explicitly digital with a computer screen and keyboard or they can be more hidden, as with the mobile phone. The power of computers has increased dramatically in recent times and with it so has the number and use of digital modes in amateur radio.

The IBM PC was initially an expensive desktop computer aimed at the business world but, when IBM lost the exclusivity of its product in the 1980s, prices dropped with the competition that ensued. The PC became a home and office product and with home use came music and entertainment. This was enhanced by the fast-developing games market, a market that demanded realism in its gaming environment and this created a demand for higher computing performance and especially better sound. The PC sound card was spawned in this environment.

Meanwhile, the amateur transceiver market was evolving from the thermionic valve-based designs of the 1960s and 1970s, such as the classic FT-101 from Yaesu, towards the fully solid-state transceivers of the 1980s. The newer designs were more stable and often had a digital frequency read-out that made tuning to an exact frequency much easier.

In the late 1990s, Peter Martinez, G3PLX, designed a new digital mode that combined the functionality of the PC with its sound card and the solid-state transceiver. This mode was to improve on the performance of RTTY over a noisy HF channel and use commonly-available equipment: PSK31 was born. It used phase shift keying of the RF carrier that proved to be more immune to noise and it had a very narrow bandwidth. It was very successful and paved the way for more PC sound card based modes.

In 2001 Professor Joe Taylor, K1JT, **Fig 1.1**, designed a new digital mode, FSK441, that was aimed at meteor scatter QSOs using a PC sound card, interface and a VHF transceiver. Professor Taylor is a Nobel Prize-winning astrophysicist from Princeton University, USA, who then went on to develop the WSJT software package aimed at weak-signal applications. The WSJT modes all use state-of-the-art digital communications technology including error control.

Fig 1.1: Professor Joe Taylor, K1JT, the developer of the WSJT suite of programs and 'inventor' of FT8.

WSJT was replaced by WSJT-X ('Weak Signal Communication by K1JT'), which is freeware and distributed under the Open GNU licence. Whilst FSK441 was the first mode, there are now many more and, with the advent of FT8, WSJT-X has become one of the dominant software packages in amateur digital modes. When WSJT-X version 2.0 was released it evolved from the relatively exotic meteor scatter and moonbounce activities into mainstream HF DXing.

HF digital modes can be categorised in several ways, by their message – is it free format or a fixed format; by their speed – are they slow or fast modes; or by their input method – keyboard or speech. In this book, we will be considering HF digital modes that have both free and fixed message structures and have keyboard input. We will not cover digital voice or the fast WSJT modes such as MSK144.

In Chapter 2 we will discuss how to set up an HF digital station, what equipment you will need and how to configure it. To make this as practical as possible, we concentrate on two different freely-available software packages, WSJT-X and Fldigi, and briefly discuss others such as JTDX and MSHV.

In Chapter 3 we will cover how to operate the digital station: how to use the software packages to achieve QSOs using FT8, FT4 and PSK31.

In Chapter 4 we look at two new free format 'keyboard-to-keyboard' modes: JS8 and VarAC.

For those who wish to know more about how digital modes work, in Chapter 5 we discuss the technical aspects of digital modes and explain some of the ways they achieve their impressive performance.

2. Building a Digital Modes Station

In this chapter, we discuss building a digital modes station. Most, if not all, of the components will be present in the average radio amateur's shack already. The main components are a transceiver, complete with power supply and antenna, and a computer. A simple interface between the two might also be needed.

TRANSCEIVERS

The primary requirements for a transceiver to be capable of using digital modes are the same as those for SSB and CW: frequency stability and an output transmission low in harmonics. This means that most if not all transceivers produced in the last 20 years or so are acceptable, providing the older ones still meet their original specifications regarding the two primary requirements. Power output is less important for digital modes than for SSB or CW, so even low-power transceivers can be used to good effect. Sophisticated digital processing is also of less importance since speech processing and noise-reduction functions are turned off when in digital mode. It is perfectly possible to build your own transceiver and use it rather than buying a commercial product: digital modes have not disrupted the amateur's ability to do homebrew.

The simplest and most universal method of interfacing to your transceiver to use digital modes is through the microphone input, PTT and headphone output connectors, which are often on the front panel. All transceivers will have these connections. A direct connection is possible, but it is better to provide some form of interface and this will be discussed later.

As computers evolved, their connectivity has improved and it is the same with transceivers. Older transceivers just have Accessory sockets on the back panel that allow audio in and out as well as the PTT function. The link is basically analogue audio and a simple PTT switching voltage. They are usually round DIN-type connectors. Serial ports using 9-pin D connectors became common, but these were used mainly for computer control of the transceiver (CAT) and not analogue sound in and out. Finally, transceivers began using the Universal Serial Bus (USB – not to be confused with upper side band!).

Current transceivers, like those in **Fig 2.1** are especially easy to use in digital modes but they often have an assortment of rear connections that can be confusing. The terminology for these connections can be confusing because they are called by different names and have slightly different functionality: Computer Aided Transceiver (CAT), Accessory socket, sometimes abbreviated to 'ACC', Data socket, USB port and COM port just to name a few. It is necessary to read the user manuals, and sometimes even the service manuals, to gain an understanding of which connection does what and how to connect to it.

Fig 2.1: Modern transceivers: top, the Icom IC-7300, below, the Yaesu FTdx3000.

Fig 2.2: Yaesu FTdx10 back panel.

A quick glance at the back panel of any modern transceiver will show you what is available. For example, **Fig 2.2** shows the back panel of the Yaesu FTdx10 and you can see that there are several possibilities for connection: RTTY / DATA, ACC, one USB-B and two USB-A connectors and an RS-232C connector (as well as connections for the antenna, external speaker, key, linear amplifier etc). You might assume that the RTTY / DATA would be the most appropriate, but this turns out to be a connection dedicated to RTTY and not to data in general. In this case, both the RS-232C and USB-B connectors allow the transceiver to be interfaced to a PC.

Since the latest type of connection is USB it is well worth investigating. Transceivers such as the Yaesu FT-991 and the Icom IC-7300 feature USB ports that provide both the sound card and the CAT serial control link over a single cable. However, this is not always obvious from the user manuals. Using the transceiver's USB port connection may require you to download specific USB drivers associated with the model of transceiver and install these on your computer. Once you have done this you can directly access the sound card and CAT serial link within the transceiver and no other interface or connection is required.

In summary, there are three potential ways of connecting your transceiver to your computer: via the microphone and headphone sockets, via accessory sockets on the back panel and via USB. All but the USB socket connection will require an additional interface.

SETTING UP THE COMPUTER

The modern amateur station will undoubtedly have some form of computer and typically this will be a PC, either a desktop model or, perhaps more likely, a notebook. It might be a Windows machine, a Mac or a Linux-based computer. Any of these will do to establish a digital modes station, but here we will concentrate upon Windows as this is probably more common and also setting up under the other operating systems is very similar in concept with only a few differences in procedures. Surprisingly, despite the complexity of the software, it is not necessary to have a particularly powerful computer. The specifications for running the latest version of WSJT-X, v.2.6, released in January 2023, are as follows:

- Operating system: Windows 7 or later, MacOS 10.13 or later, or Linux;
- 1.5GHz CPU or faster;
- 200Mb of available memory;
- Monitor with at least 1024 x 780 resolution;
- Audio system with a sampling rate of 48,000 samples per second at 16-bit resolution;
- A means for synchronising the computer clock to UTC within ±1 second.

The audio system does not need to be an expensive state-of-the-art device since most internal sound systems will work fine and, failing an internal solution, a cheap external USB sound card will be just as good. If you are using a sound system that is part of your transceiver you will need special drivers. These are available from the manufacturer as a free download.

Fig 2.3: Windows Sound Control panel.

The Windows 10 PC sound system is configured using the Sound control panel that is found under the Settings tab, itself found by right clicking the bottom left Windows logon button.

Fig 2.3 shows the sound configuration screen. This has three tabs of interest: Playback, Recording and Sounds. The Playback tab shows the current configuration of the speaker output; here it shows that the USB Audio Device is selected. If you are using an internal sound device this screen will only show that device since in the case shown in **Fig 2.3**

there are two sound devices: an internal device, Realtek, and an external USB Audio device, so there is a choice to be made. Make sure you select the one connected to your radio! If you only have one sound device, it is important to prevent Windows from sending its system sounds to your radio, so it is advisable to select "no sound" under the Sounds tab also found on this screen. If you have a dedicated sound card for digital mode operation, make sure it is not selected as the Windows default playback device but is only selected by your digital modes operating software.

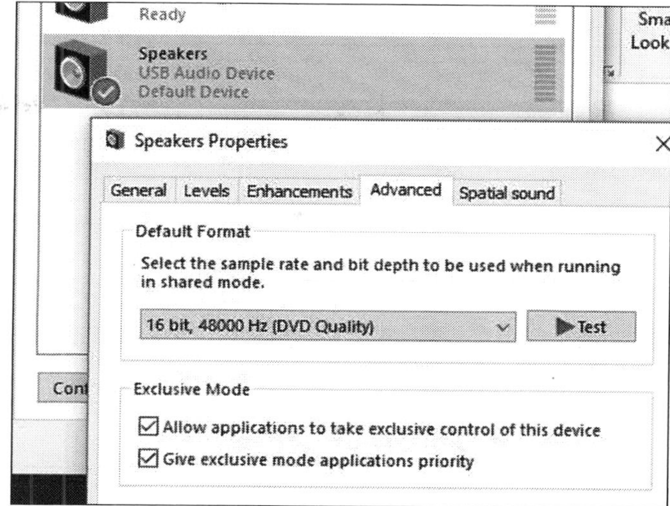

Fig 2.4: Windows sound sample rate and bit depth.

If you double click on the device in the list further configuration options are available. Here you can select the audio sampling rate and bit depth, for example, WSJT-X software uses 16-bit and 48,000Hz. It is worth checking that this is set up correctly here as well: see **Fig 2.4.**

Normally you will not need to install a new driver for your sound device. You either use the one that is already configured in your PC or the one automatically loaded when you plug in your USB sound device. However, if you are using a modern transceiver with a built-in sound card you will most likely need to install a special driver specific to that transceiver. Consult the user guide for your transceiver to see how to do this. Usually this just involves downloading the driver's installation setup file from the manufacturer's website and running this in order to install the driver.

SETTING UP THE TRANSCEIVER FOR DIGITAL MODES

The most direct way to set up digital modes is to use an external interface connected to the microphone input, headphone output and PTT on your transceiver.

Here you measure and adjust the input and output levels from your computer and radio; you have total control. However, modern transceivers will offer you several other options. They often have a socket on the rear panel that allows audio in / out and PTT that is dedicated to data modes. As explained earlier, unfortunately, there is no common terminology for these sockets, so it is a mat-

Menu			
031	CAT rate	4800	
032	CAT TOT	100mS	
033	CAT RTS	Enable	
060	PC keying PTT	Off	
062	Data Mode	OTHERS	
064	OTHER DISP	1500Hz	This affects the dial frequency vs actual frequency
065	OTHER SHIFT	1500Hz	
070	DATA IN SELECT	REAR	
071	DATA PTT SELECT	RTS	
072	DATA PORT SELECT	USB	

Table 2.1: Typical menu parameters for FT8 on Yaesu FT-891.

ter of reading the radio's manual and, to make matters worse, often the manuals are not very clear in this respect either. It is worth investigating internet forums for both your radio and for the digital mode software that you are attempting to use. For WSJT-X users **https://groups.io/g/WSJTX** is a good starting place as is **https://groups.io/g/winfldigi** for Fldigi software users.

Having an idea of what you are trying to achieve when you set up your transceiver does help. The setup can be viewed as a two-stage process: setting up the radio's communication channel and setting up the radio's RF performance. In modern transceivers this is done using the menu structure pertinent to the radio in question. Each manufacturer has its own terminology so if you move between major manufacturers you will need to learn the new terms.

Table 2.1 shows the menu parameters that need to be adjusted on a Yaesu FT-991 transceiver for FT8. In addition to these menu settings, the mode needs to be selected: MODE DATA-USB. Several of the receiver options also need to be adjusted: DNR is OFF, DNF is OFF. On the transmit side DTGAIN is adjusted to avoid over-driving the PA.

INTERFACING TRANSCEIVERS AND COMPUTERS

Unless you are using your transceiver's internal sound card, connected via USB, you will need an interface between computer and transceiver. The purpose is to isolate the two devices and reduce the possibility of feedback loops or even damage to either device.

A simple interface circuit can be constructed by various techniques and the layout is not critical, but you should take care both to maintain the isolation and

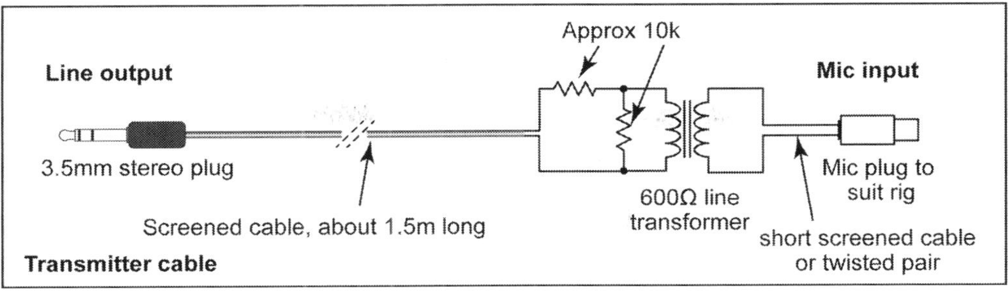

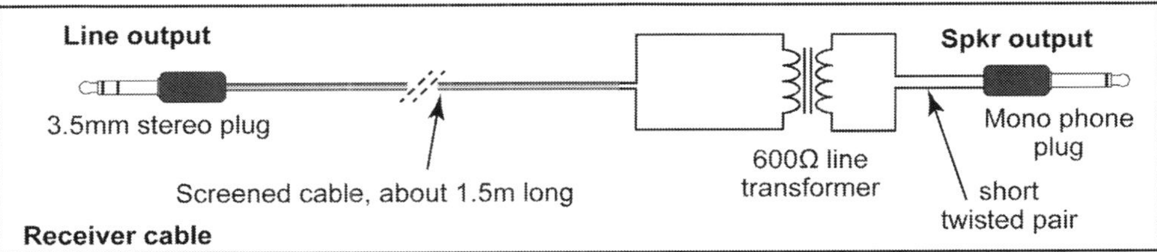

Fig 2.5: Simple interface circuit.

to screen the interface to prevent RF interference. A simple circuit is shown in **Fig 2.5**. The use of ferrite clip-on cores on the input and output leads can help reduce interference. The simple circuit does not include a PTT connection, but this can either be done using the transceiver's VOX or by activating a simple transistor switch from the audio line output. Several designs are available on the internet.

An alternative is to purchase a commercial interface such as that shown in **Fig 2.6**. They often include a separate sound card and are connected using USB. Finally, if you do not wish to use your computer's sound system, purchase a cheap USB sound card such as the one in **Fig 2.7**. These are available on the internet for less than £10.

Fig 2.6: SignaLink USB interface from Tigertronics.

Fig 2.7: An external USB sound card powered by the USB connection.

TIME SERVERS

As we will see later, it is important to set the computer's real-time clock to an accuracy of a few tenths of a second. This is best achieved using a time server. A free solution is to download and install a Network Time Protocol server such as Meinberg: **https://www.meinbergglobal.com/english/info/ntp.htm**

Although this was originally a Unix application, it is now available for Windows and is easily installed using a wizard. Although you can get some idea of the accuracy of your real time clock from the command line interface using Meinberg, another useful web resource is Time.is, as shown in **Fig 2.8**.

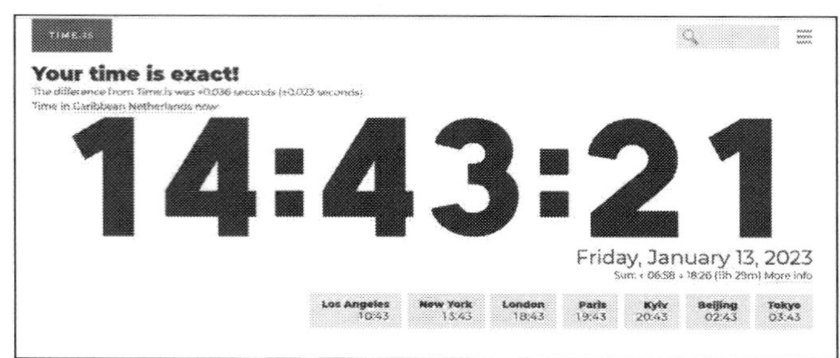

Fig 2.8: Checking your time.

SETTING UP WSJT-X SOFTWARE

The WSJT-X software is a comprehensive application that allows communication on all the weak-signal modes: FT8, FT4, JT4, JT9, JT65, Q65, FST4, FST4W, MSK144 as well as WSPR ('Weak Signal Propagation Reporter') and Echo, a mode specific to moonbounce. A new version with extensive enhancements, version 2.6, was released in January 2023 and is available as a free download from **https://sourceforge.net/projects/wsjt/files/**

There are versions for Windows, Linux and OS X, so just select the one you need. The earlier version 2.0 was a major upgrade from previous versions and since the FT8 protocol has changed it is not backwards compatible with previous versions of WSJT when running FT8 (or MSK144, but we are not covering that mode here). The Windows installation is easy using the usual installation wizard as shown in **Fig 2.9**. You just run the downloaded file and follow the prompts.

Fig 2.9: WSJT-X setup.

On running the software you should see

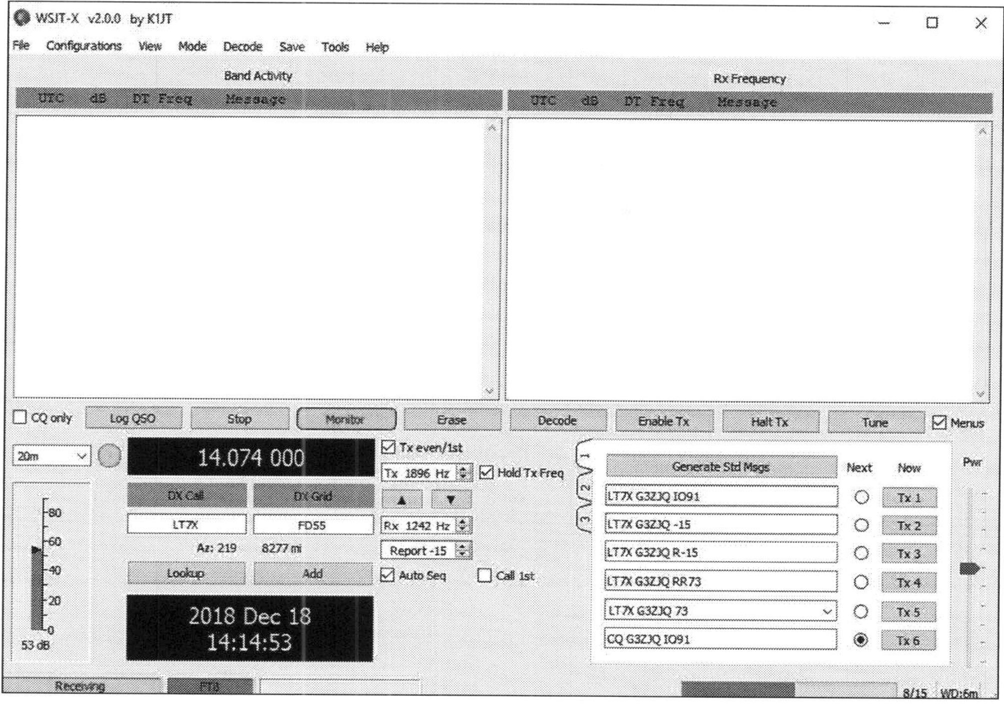

Fig 2.10: WSJT-X main screen.

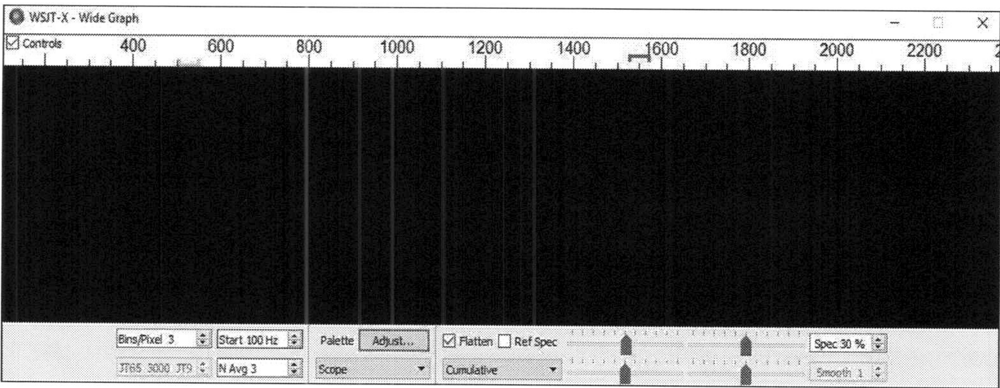

Fig 2.11: WSJT-X blank waterfall display.

the main screen, **Fig 2.10**, and the waterfall display (or 'Wide Graph'), which will still be empty, as shown in **Fig 2.11**.

You must now configure the software, so click 'File' on the menu bar at the top of the main screen then click on 'Settings', or you could use the F2 speed

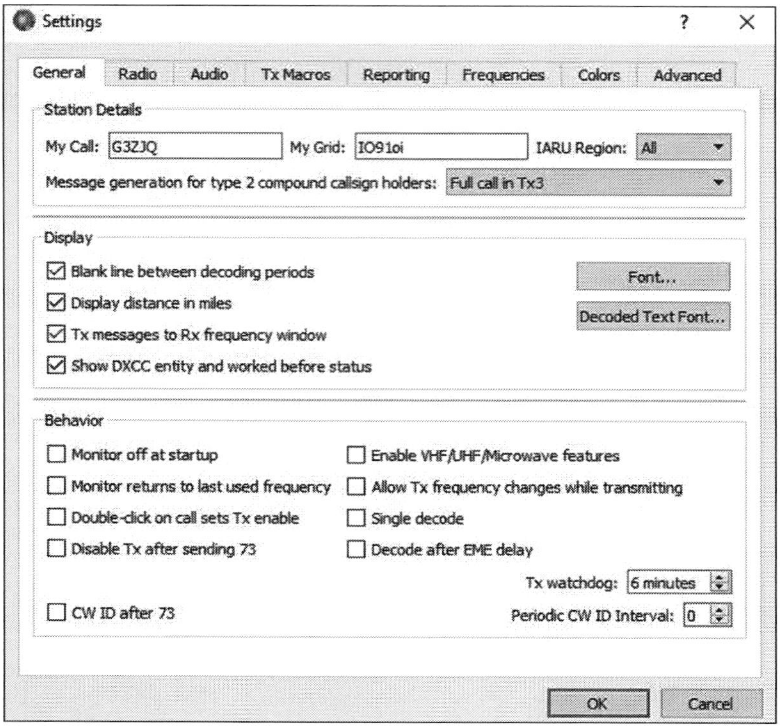

Fig 2.12: General settings.

key. Start by selecting the 'General' tab, **Fig 2.12**, and enter your callsign and Maidenhead locator. Next select 'Radio' and enter your radio model using the pull-down list, **Fig 2.13**, set the COM port, and the appropriate serial port settings for your radio's interface.

Finally, make sure you have the correct audio card / codec selected. Go to the 'Audio' tab, see **Fig 2.14**, and use the pull-down menus to select the correct codec.

Select FT8 from the mode pull-down menu at the top of the screen. If you have set up the interface, have accurate network time and are tuned to an FT8 frequency, the waterfall and main screen will slowly become populated with the callsigns of the active stations. If this does not happen you will need to re-check your settings, but do remember that it will take a perhaps 30 seconds or so for the decoded traffic to appear.

If, after waiting a few minutes nothing has appeared, you should check your PC clock against the time service Time.is. You need to be within a second or so of the exact time. There is also an extensive help file facility accessed by pressing F1 and the *WSJT-X User Guide* is available from:
https://wsjt.sourceforge.io/wsjtx-doc/wsjtx-main-2.6.1.html

The WSJT group mentioned earlier is also a good place to get help.

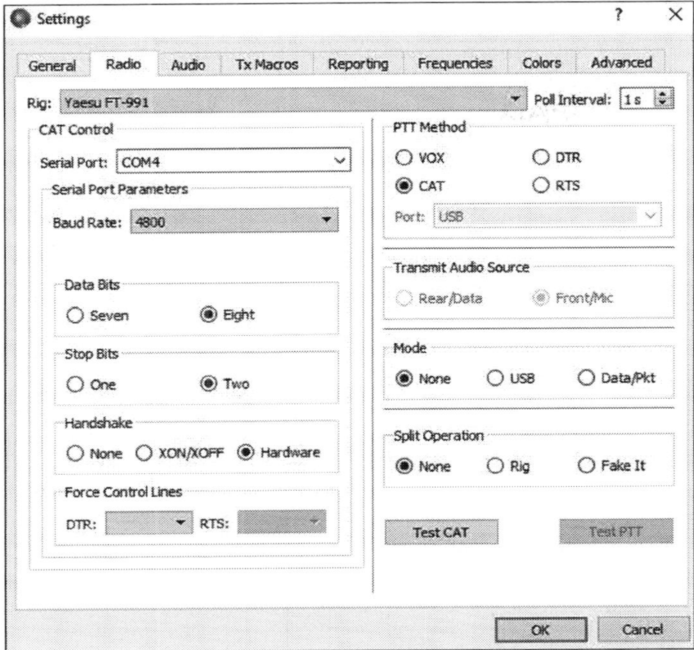

Fig 2.13: Radio settings.

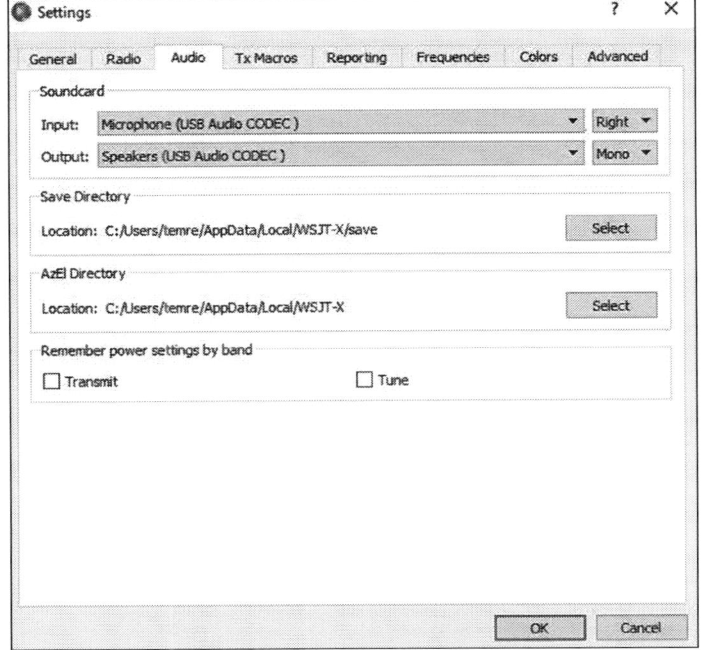

Fig 2.14: Audio settings.

OTHER PROGRAMS FOR WEAK-SIGNAL MODES

The WSJT suite of programs introduced the popular FT8 and FT4 communication protocols, or operating 'modes', to the world but there are other programs that can also be used for these weak-signal modes. Arguably the next most popular after WSJT-X is ***JTDX*** by Igor Chernikov, UA3DJY; Arvo Järve, ES1JA, and their teams. JTDX covers FT8, FT4, JT65, JT9+JT65, JT9, T10 and WSPR-2. The latest version (as of January 2023) is 2.2.159, which was released in March 2022. It can be downloaded from SourceForge by going to **https://sourceforge.net/projects/jtdx** and then clicking on 'Files'. The *JTDX User Manual* can be downloaded from the same folder.

The main focus in the development of JTDX was on the sensitivity and decoding efficiency, specifically for DX working. It has been reported that side-by-side tests showed that JTDX consistently decoded a greater number of stations than did WSJT-X. However, a new version of WSJT-X, version 2.6 released in January 2023, claimed that its decoding performance for FT8 (as well as that of another protocol,

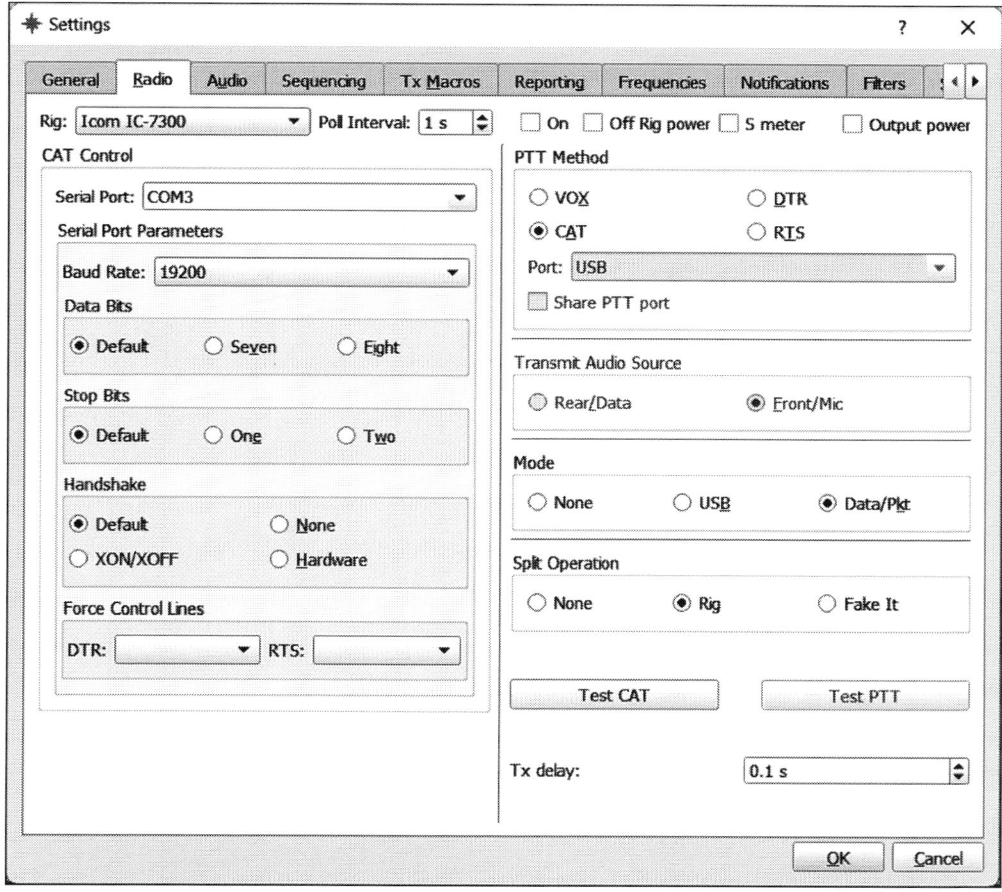

Fig 2.15: JTDX Radio settings setup screen.

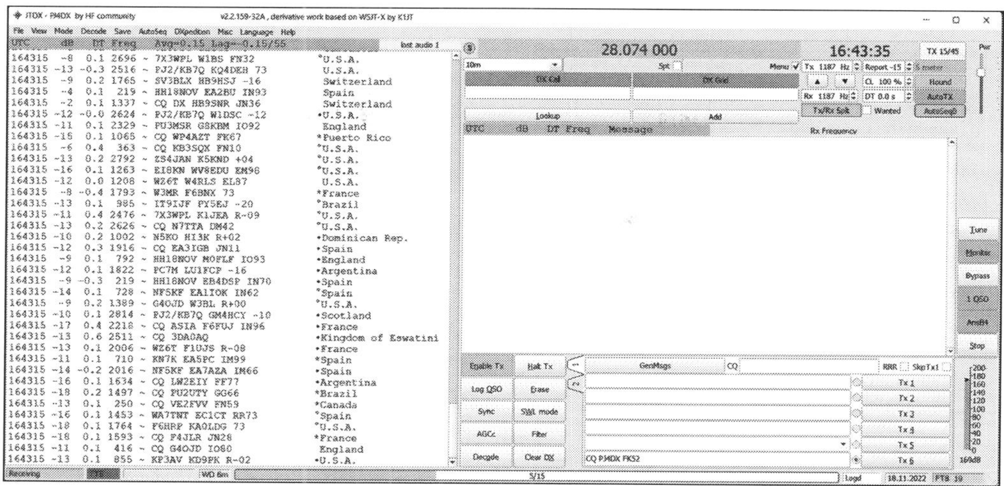

Fig 2.16: JTDX main screen, showing plenty of activity.

Q65) has been improved "in a variety of situations with available *a priori* (AP) information", so it is possible that there is now less difference in performance.

Once downloaded JTDX needs to be configured and this is done in a similar manner to that described for WSJT-X. **Fig 2.15** shows the JTDX 'Radio' setup screen (under Files –> Settings –> Radio), in this case for an Icom IC-7300.

When configured correctly and the receiver tuned to an FT8 frequency, the screen should start to fill with decodes of stations active. **Fig 2.16** shows the main JTDX screen and, as can be seen, it is quite similar to that of WSJT-X.

Another program that can be used for FT8, FT4, MSK, JTMS, FSK, ISCAT, JT6M, JT65, PI4 and Q65 is ***MSHV***, written by Christo Hristov, LZ2HV.

A typical MSHV operating screen is shown in **Fig 2.17**. DXpeditions operating on FT8 often choose to use MSHV as it allows for *multi-streaming*. When using multi-

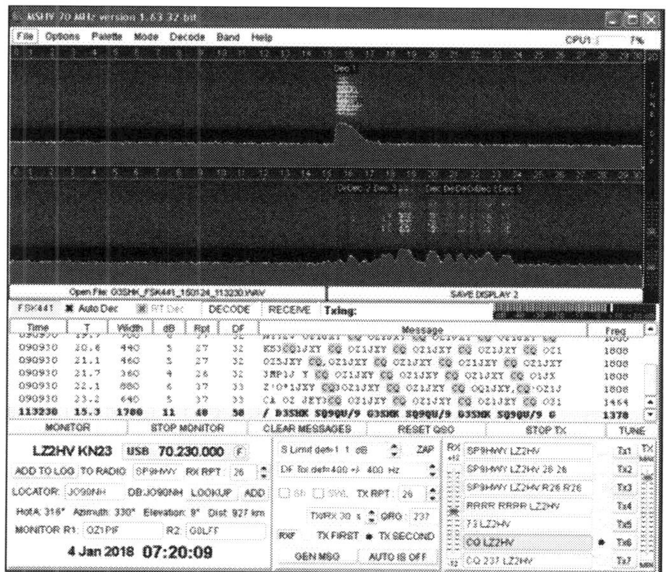

Fig 2.17: MSHV main screen (image: lz2hv.org/mshv website).

streaming the DXped-ition can respond to many stations in a single 15-second transmit period, as opposed to just the one in both JTDX and *normal* WSJT-X operation (though WSJT-X does allow for multi-streaming in its so-called 'Fox and Hound' mode, described in the next chapter).

As of January 2023 the latest version of MSHV is 2.69 and it can be downloaded from **http://lz2hv.org/mshv**

SETTING UP FLDIGI SOFTWARE

Although WSJT-X, JTDX and MSHV are very comprehensive software packages, they only cover the WSJT weak-signal modes. If you want to operate using any other of the myriad digital modes, including PSK, MFSK, RTTY, Hell, DominoEX, Olivia, Throb and even CW, you will need to install more software. ***Fldigi***, which is an acronym for Fast Light Digital modem application, is a comprehensive open source freeware package that is available for download from SourceForge at: **https://sourceforge.net/projects/fldigi/** It is available for Windows, Linux, Mac OS and Android. The minimum recommended CPU speed is 1.2 – 1.6GHz, which is not much of a limitation with modern computers. The Windows version will run under any version of Windows after Win 2000.

The current (January 2023) Windows version is 4.1.23 and if you download the setup file and run it you should see the opening screen shown in **Fig 2.18**.

There are four windows. The white top left window is the browser window and it will show activity across the full 3kHz audio bandwidth. The yellow window is the received window and it is here that the decoded messages will be displayed. The cyan (light blue) window is the transmit window. It is here that you will type your messages to be sent. The lower black window is the waterfall display. The two thin vertical lines on the waterfall indicate the frequency that you are tuned to: both receiving and transmitting.

There are three command ribbons. The top one has the usual File tab followed by OpMode, Configure, View, Logbook and Help. The second command ribbon, beginning with CQ, is a way of accessing the macros; these are common text messages that you can create. The lowest command ribbon controls the waterfall.

Before you can use the software, it must be configured. Configuration is in several stages:

- Enter your station's details;
- Set up the audio card;
- Set up the CAT control of your transceiver;
- Set up the waterfall;
- Set up the TX audio level.

You can open the station details configuration page by going to: Configure –> UI –> Operator.

You just enter your details in the page as shown in **Fig 2.19**.

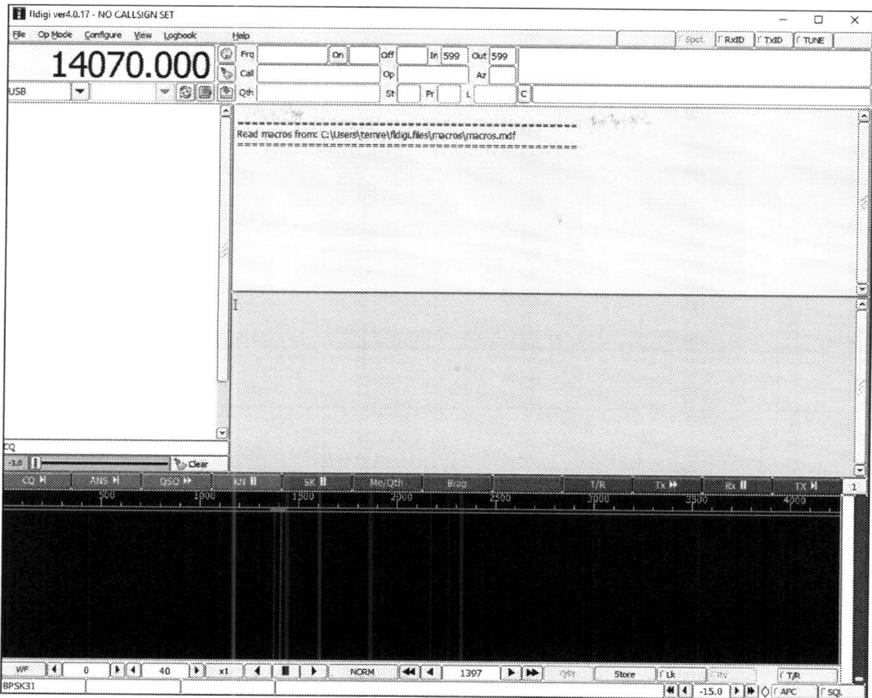

Fig 2.18: Fldigi first time screen.

Fig 2.19: Operator details.

Next, we set up the audio: Configure –> Sound Card. This is shown in **Fig 2.20**. This is set up with the same information as that used in the WSJT-X setup (since the rig is the same). CAT control is next and here Fldigi has several options but since this is to work with the same transceiver as WSJT we can use the same CAT techniques as previously, as shown in **Fig 2.21** under the 'Hamlib' tab. We get to this configuration page by Configure –> Rig Control.

Notice that the selections are the same as the WSJT-X configuration and include the COM port, Baud rate, stop bits, flow control and PTT selection.

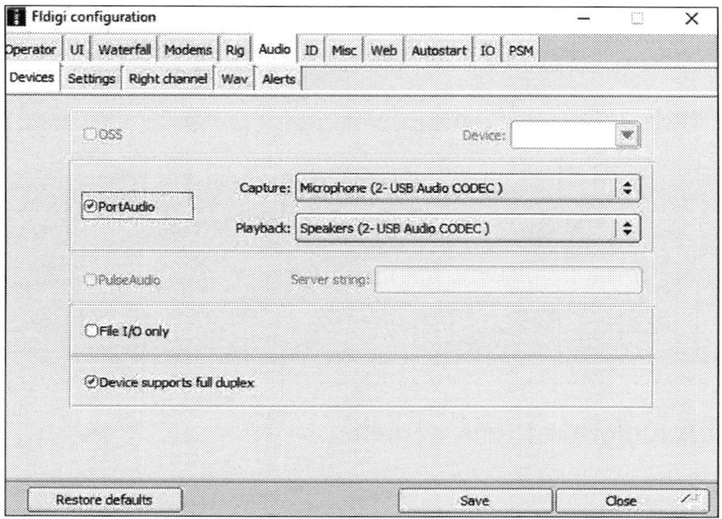

Fig 2.20: Sound card configuration.

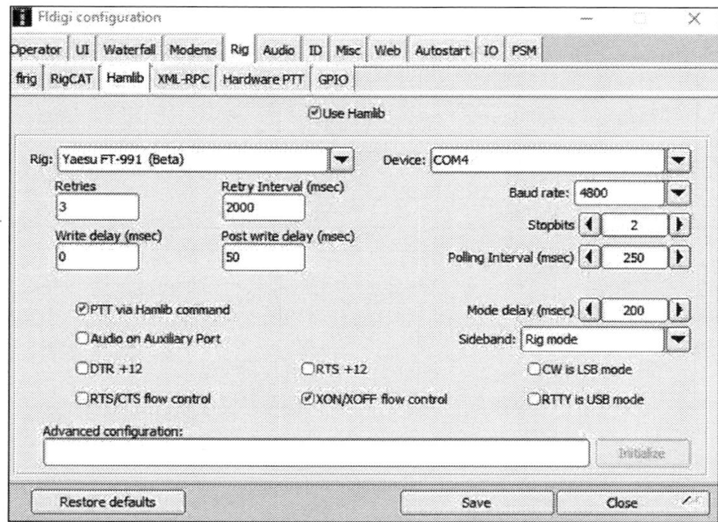

Fig 2.21: Rig control configuration.

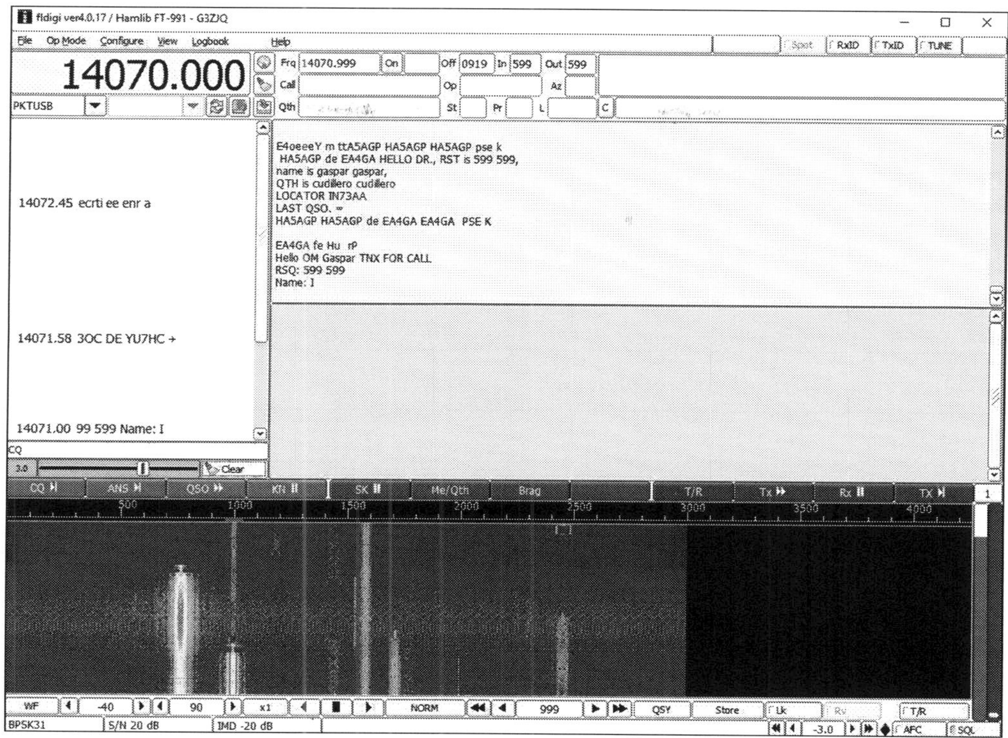

Fig 2.22: Fldigi decoding BPSK31.

Even now that the software is receiving audio from the transceiver the waterfall is probably blank. The initial dynamic range of the waterfall is set from 0dB with a range of 40dB. Since we are using 16-bit audio we can adjust the range to 90dB: this is done in the second box from the left in the command ribbon beneath the waterfall. You can now adjust the bottom level until the waterfall noise floor appears. If you now select the mode by OpMode –> BPSK31 and choose a frequency where BPSK31 is to be expected, you should now see something like that shown in **Fig 2.22**.

SUMMARY

In this chapter we have discussed building a station to operate using digital modes. We discussed transceivers and found that most of them can be pressed into digital mode service without modification. The key requirement of a computer was discussed at some length and we concluded that the requirements were minimal and that most shack computers could be used. We discussed the options concerning interfacing computers to transceivers and offered some simple solutions. Finally, we covered the installation and basic configuration of some popular software packages.

RSGB BOOKSHOP

Always the best Amateur Radio books

HF DX Basics

By Steve Telenius-Lowe, PJ4DX

Will sunspot cycle 25 be one of the strongest on record?

One thing that is certain is that when propagation improves, contacting far flung parts of the world (DX) on the High Frequency bands (HF) becomes easier and much more of a pleasure. It remains one of the enduring fascinations of amateur radio.

HF DX Basics provides a practical guide to making the most of this endlessly fascinating area of operation. Many are put off by the challenges of DX operation but well-known author and DXer Steve Telenius-Lowe, PJ4DX dispels the myths about huge antennas and high power in an easy-to-understand way. Based on Steve's previous book *HF SSB DX Basics* this book provides a guide to what DX is all about and you are led through to the opportunities the HF bands provide and much more. *HF DX Basics* has been revised to bring it fully up-to-date and much new material about FT8 operating as well as details of operating in the 1.8, 5, 10 and 50MHz bands has been added.

As you would expect you will find a practical guide to what antennas make good choices in your location, choosing your transceiver including what the myriad of buttons on a modern transceiver do. There is a guide to the HF bands you can operate, their propagation characteristics and what to expect from them. Steve also provides practical advice on how to avoid pitfalls when operating on the bands and much more including handling pile-ups, split working, QRP operation, QSLs and even being DX yourself.
So, give HF DXing a try and allow the DX 'bug' to bite!

HF DX Basics is for anyone interested in operating in the hugely satisfying area of DX amateur radio by providing advice and practical steps to improve your station and get you started DXing.

Size: 174 x 240mm, 144 pages
ISBN: 9781913995225
ONLY £11.99

www.rsgbshop.org

on orders over £30. See T&Cs

Radio Society of Great Britain, 3 Abbey Court, Priory Business Park, Bedford, MK44 3WH Tel: 01234 8327

3. Operating Digital Modes

Having set up your transceiver, connected the interface (if necessary) and loaded the software package, you are very nearly ready to get going with your first QSO. We covered the installation and basic configuration of several software packages in the previous chapter. In this chapter we will see how to use these packages and enter the world of HF digital. As with many software packages, the supplied instructions can be confusing for those who are new to data modes. It is for this reason that we will go into some detail, in the hope that this might help overcome any confusion. However, the software packages will change over time and they may alter their user interfaces from those shown here. Hopefully this will not be too different!

It is worth mentioning that you can achieve very good results, sometimes even surprising results, using modest antennas and low power. The power duty-cycle using digital modes is much larger than that of SSB and, as such, it is well worth keeping the power level down to avoid overloading the PA. Most transceivers have a power output rating that is intended for SSB operation and thus should be reduced for high duty-cycle digital modes.

This chapter starts by considering where in the amateur HF bands you can find digital modes being used. It then discusses in some detail how to operate the software using FT8 as an example mode. We then discuss operating a keyboard mode using Fldigi and BPSK31.

DIGITAL MODES' FREQUENCIES

Although digital modes can be operated throughout most of the amateur bands the band plans do specify frequency allocations for these modes. In the UK, digital modes are to be found together with other narrow bandwidth modes in the bottom part of the allocated band. The active frequencies for the various data modes tend to be based on legacy use as the bands are not sub-divided

Band	FT8	FT4	JT65	PSK	JS8	VarAC
160m	**1840**	—	1838	1838	1842	1995
80m	**3573**	3575	3570	3570	3578	3595
	3567		3576	3580		
	3585					
*60m	**5357**	—	5357	—	—	5355
	5362					
40m	**7074**	7047.5	7071	7040	7078	7105
	7056					
	7071					
	7080					
30m	**10136**	10140	10138	10142	10130	10133
	10131					
	10133					
	10143					
20m	**14074**	14080	14076	14070	14078	14105
	14071					
	14090					
17m	**18100**	18104	18102	18097	18104	18107
	18095					
15m	**21074**	21140	21076	21070	21078	21105
	21091			21080		
12m	**24915**	24919	24917	24920	24922	24927
	24911					
10m	**28074**	28180	28076	28120	28078	28105
	28095			28070		
6m	**50313**	50318	50276	50290	50318	50330
	50323		50310	50305		
	50310					

Table 3.1: Spot frequencies for various digital modes. *NB: In the UK only Full licensees may use 5MHz frequencies.

into specific data modes. The spot frequencies where some of the digital modes can be found are shown in **Table 3.1**. The FT8 frequencies shown in **bold** are the main operating frequencies used; the alternative frequencies below are often used by stations using WSJT-X Fox and Hound or MSHV DXpedition (multi-streaming) mode. The PSK frequencies shown cover BPSK31 as well as other PSK variants. It will be noticed that some of the listed frequencies coincide with, or overlap, frequencies used by the other modes and none of the frequencies in the table should be considered to be 'set in stone'. Due to the rapid development of FT8 (in particular) the frequencies used by other modes are rather fluid. The table should be viewed in conjunction with the current IARU / RSGB band plans published annually in *RadCom* and available on the RSGB website at **https://rsgb.org/main/operating/band-plans/**: As of early 2023 the HF digital mode band plans are being reviewed by the IARU which will likely result in some changes to the band plans in coming years.

OPERATING FT8 USING WSJT-X / JTDX

In this section operating using the WSJT-X program is used as an example. Operating with JTDX is similar, but examples are given where its operation differs markedly from that of WSJT-X.

Now that you have completed the basic configuration and the software is working, you can explore the different modes. Let's start with the most popular mode: FT8. If you have followed the previous sections configuration and you are tuned to an active FT8 frequency, the waterfall should look something like **Fig 3.1**, which shows the waterfall, and **Fig 3.2**, which shows the main decode window. Note that these are separate windows and can be moved around independently. If you can hear the characteristic FT8 sounds coming from your transceiver, but no signals appear on the waterfall, check that the 'Monitor' button is green, and that your computer clock is accurate, using Time.is.

The waterfall in **Fig 3.1** shows several FT8 signals spread out over the frequency range of the audio from your receiver, while the black box on the main window shows the frequency to which the transceiver is set. Since we are set to USB-DATA (or just USB if you are using the microphone input) the actual frequencies of the FT8 transmissions are the sum of the frequency in the box on the main window, 14.074, and the scale along the top of the waterfall.

The 'Band Activity' box at the left of the screen shows all the decoded FT8 signals within the audio passband, while the 'Rx Frequency' box at the right of the screen shows just those within the Rx window, defined by the green U-shaped cursor that is on the waterfall scale. The red U-shaped cursor shows the transmit frequency, again on the frequency scale. You can move these cursors around

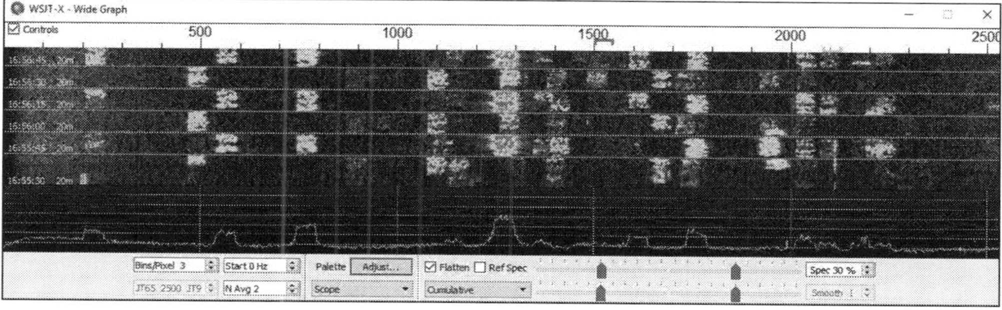

Fig 3.1: WSJT-X 'Wide Graph' or waterfall, showing several FT8 signals.

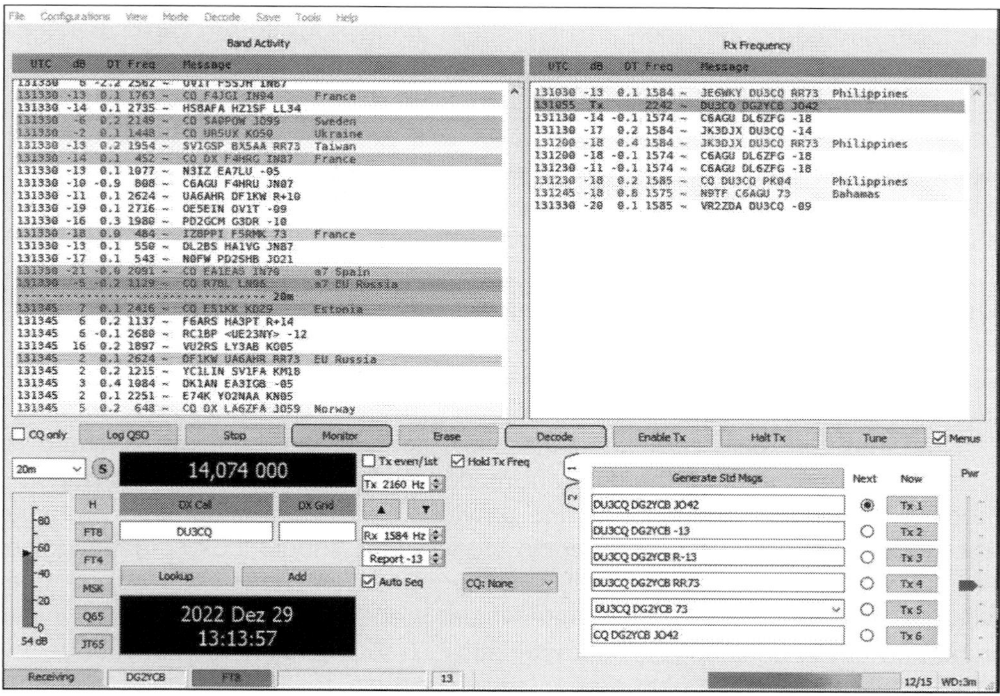

Fig 3.2: WSJT-X (v2.6) main window (image: https://sourceforge.net/projects/wsjt/).

by just clicking on the waterfall to move the Rx cursor, Shift-click to move the Tx cursor and Ctrl-click to move both. These and other special mouse commands can be seen by pressing F5. If using JTDX, a left click of the mouse moves the receive cursor and a right click moves the transmit cursor.

The waterfall clearly shows the 15-second odd and even periodicity of the FT8 signal, e.g. at approximately 550Hz and 770Hz. You can identify the stations by comparing the frequency given in the waterfall to that in the decoded Band Activity box or by placing the receive cursor over the frequency of interest. The individual time periods are listed to the left next to the band in use.

The overall scale of the waterfall is governed in the horizontal scale by the Bins / Pixel, Start frequency and by the N Avg in the vertical (time) scale. You can also stretch the window itself. The graph beneath the waterfall, the spectrum window, shows the signal strength in dB.

Entries in the Band Activity and Rx Activity boxes can be colour coded to highlight CQ calls and other attributes listed under File –> Settings –> Colours (or File –> Settings –> Notifications in JTDX). Each entry gives the UTC time, signal strength, time delta (difference) from your clock, frequency and the message itself. Messages in FT8 are very structured and give basic QSO information: callsign, locator, signal report and acknowledgement.

One final adjustment on the receive side is to set the receive levels for opti-

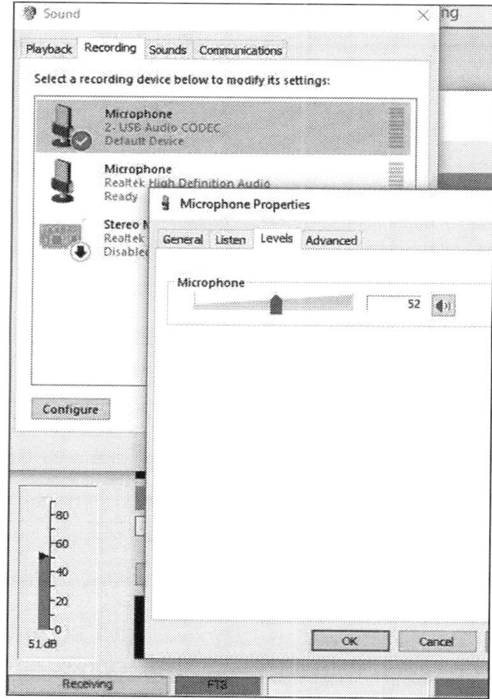

Fig 3.3: Windows 10 input sound levels.

mum FT8 decoding. This is done by adjusting the audio input to the sound card to make the WSJT level indicator range between 30 and 50dB (between 60 and 70dB or 160 to 170dB in JTDX, depending on the version). This can be done in several ways: within Windows, within your transceiver or perhaps even using your interface. The aim is not to have any one adjustment set to maximum so that linearity and distortion is avoided.

In Windows 10 you can find the sound control panel under Settings –> System –> Sound. **Fig 3.3** is a composite screen shot showing the Windows sound control panel overlaid on the WSJT main window. It shows the microphone input level set to a mid-range value of 52 and the WSJT level varying around 50dB. Notice that the active sound device is the USB Codec since I am using an external sound card. If I was using the internal card and an external interface to the transceiver's microphone socket, then it would be the Realtek microphone that was active and being adjusted. If you are using a data audio output socket on your rig, there may also be an adjustment within the transceiver to consider; this is usually accessed via a menu setting: Data Output Level. Set this to mid-range as well.

Before moving on to a live QSO, now is a good time to set the transmit power level. This is done by adjusting the audio input to the transceiver. It is important to set the transmit levels such that the audio frequency part of the transmit chain is operating linearly. If you do not do this correctly, you are in danger of producing distortion products.

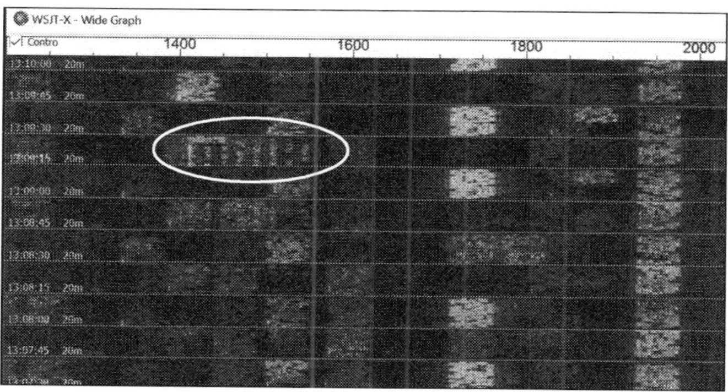

Fig 3.4: Transmission showing third harmonic distortion.

Fig 3.4 shows a par-

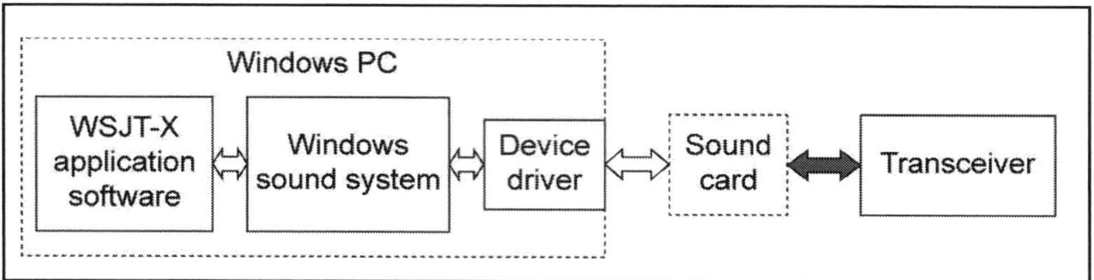

Fig 3.5: Audio chain.

tial screen shot taken from the waterfall of an FT8 third harmonic distortion product. This can be recognised by its bandwidth: it is 150Hz wide rather than the 50Hz of the normal transmission. Note that this is a harmonic of the FT8 audio modulation rather than of the RF signal so, for example, if you are transmitting at 500Hz within the wide graph waterfall this harmonic will be at 1500Hz (and it is likely that the second harmonic will also be present at 1000Hz).

To avoid producing harmonics you must adjust the audio level. However, this is not a single control but can be three or more independent but sequential controls. A block diagram of the audio chain is shown in **Fig 3.5**. The sound card is shown as a dotted box since it can be either within the computer or within the transceiver. This figure might look strange since it only refers to software blocks and the relationship to the audio is hidden. This is because most of the audio chain is digital and hence software controlled. Only the interface between the sound card and the transceiver is analogue and this can be inside the transceiver or represent an interface external to the transceiver.

There is an audio level software slider on the right-hand side of both the main WSJT-X and JTDX screens marked 'Pwr'. Windows has a complete audio system that has another software slider that controls the audio output of the sound card and, finally, there is an audio level control within the transceiver that may or may not be software controlled. If you are using an analogue audio input and interface you might also have a further audio level control there as well!

So how do you adjust all these controls? I suggest the following procedure:

1. Adjust the 'Pwr' slider in the WSJT-X / JTDX main screen to mid-range.
2. Adjust the audio output level (speakers) to midrange. In Windows 10 it is found in the same place as the microphone level adjustment explained previously.
3. If your transceiver has an output power setting / adjustment set this to a few watts. I use a 10W setting during setup.
4. Connect your transceiver to a dummy load via a power meter / VSWR bridge.
5. Click on the 'Tune' button in WSJT-X / JTDX and monitor the power output of your transceiver:
    a. If the power output as measured by the power meter matches what you

have set in (3) decrease the audio level control within your transceiver until it starts to decrease the output power;
b. If the power output as measured by the power meter is less than what you have set in (3) increase the audio level control within your transceiver until it just matches the set power.
6. Monitor the ALC level on your transceiver whilst you complete (5). It should not be excessive.

This procedure works most of the time, but a better procedure would be to monitor your actual transmission. This is easily accomplished if you have a second independent receiver such as a cheap SDR dongle and some free SDR software. You will need to avoid overloading this monitoring receiver, so a well-defined sampler is required. There are many designs for RF samplers available on the internet or in books. Some are quite complex constructions requiring metal working facilities but, for our purposes, a simple construction is adequate. **Fig 3.6** shows a very simple design that can be constructed from three connectors, a small box and a length of wire. It does not maintain 50Ω throughout, but this is of less importance at HF. Note, the SMA connector is not connected to anything on the inside of the box and just uses the centre connection as a sniffer antenna. The two N connectors are linked by a short straight-through wire link. At 20m, it has a sampling loss of 80dB but this was not enough to ensure that the monitoring receiver was not overloaded so I added an additional 20dB attenuator. It is important to ensure that you do not overload your monitoring receiver since overloading may generate internal harmonics that would give you a false impression of what would otherwise be a clean signal.

Fig 3.6: HF sampler.

The final monitoring setup is shown in **Fig 3.7**. For initial setting up, I used

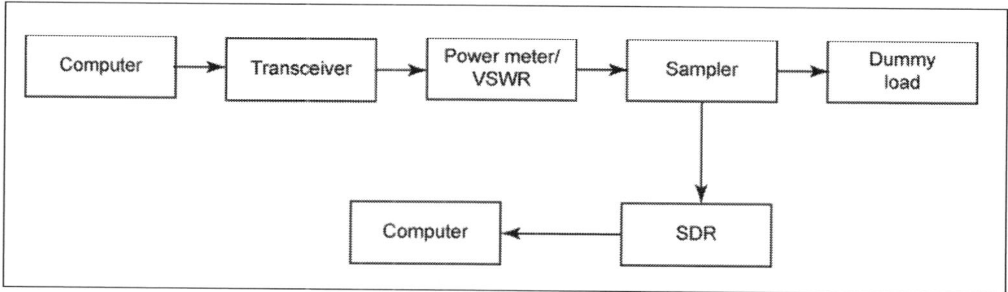

Fig 3.7: Monitoring setup.

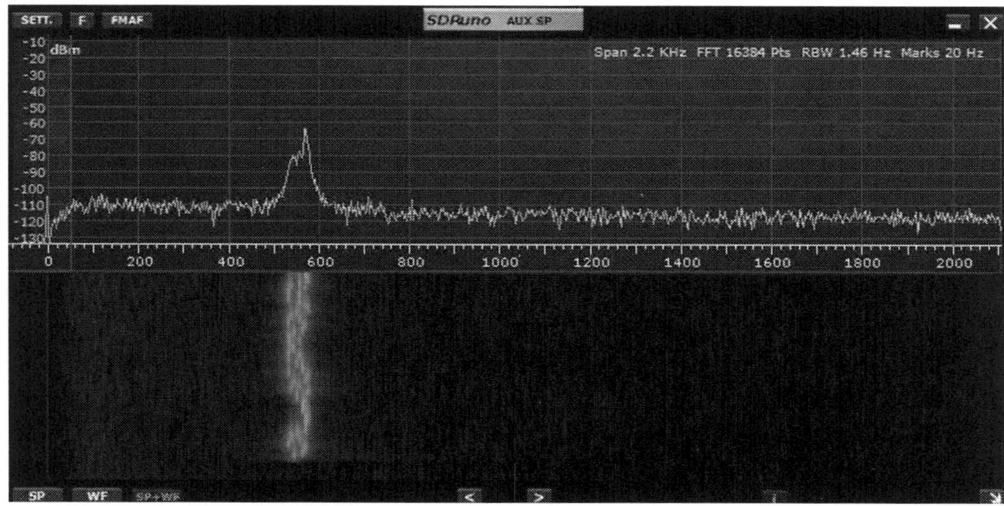

Fig 3.8: Clean FT8 signal.

a 50Ω dummy load but for long term, this can be replaced by an antenna. It is easiest to have a completely independent monitoring setup so you will need a second computer to run the SDR software. Tune the monitorlng SDR to your transmitted signal and use the spectrum display within the SDR software to examine your signal.

A clean FT8 signal without harmonics is shown in **Fig 3.8**, whilst **Fig 3.9** shows the harmonics caused by overdriving the audio stages. You can now follow the previous adjustment procedure whilst actually monitoring for any harmonic distortion.

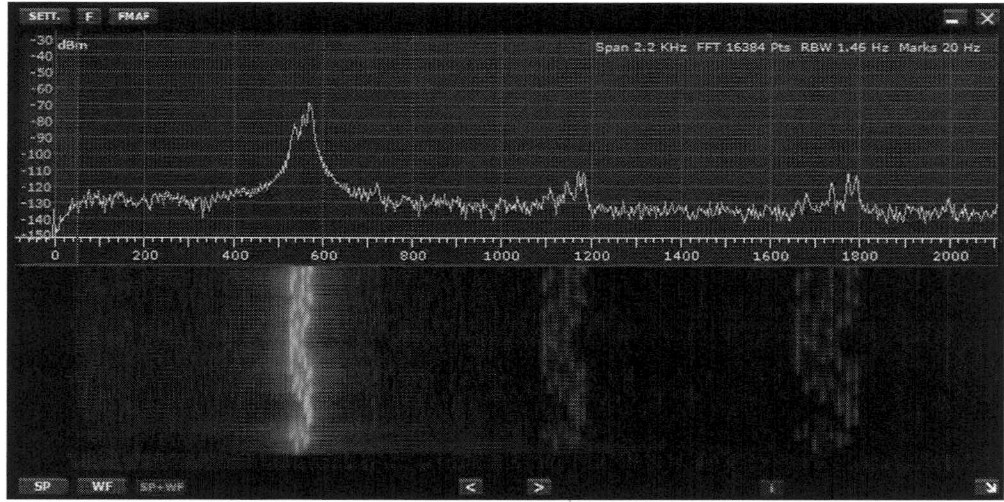

Fig 3.9: Overdriven FT8 signal showing harmonics.

If you do not have access to a suitable SDR receiver you can use a remote WebSDR. This approach will require less equipment, but you will need a second computer linked to the internet. There are several WebSDRS that can be used, and you might try several before a suitable one is found. Remember it must be able to receive your signals, so the choice is determined by time of day, distance and operating band. Most WebSDRs do not have a spectrum scope that is detailed enough to show your FT8 signal in sufficient detail to look for harmonics. So just receiving your signal is not enough and you will need to decode the FT8 as well. To do this, you need to link the WebSDR output from your browser to a decoding program such as WSJT-X.

It is possible to use the speaker output from your PC to play the SDR output from your browser and a microphone input to the same PC that is connected to the input of WSJT-X but I recommend the use of a virtual cable instead. A virtual cable is a piece of software that allows you to connect the audio output of one application directly to the input of another application running on the same computer. Several virtual cables are available for download from the internet. Once loaded, a virtual cable appears as an audio device within Windows and can be selected as an input or output in the same settings boxes as any other audio device (speakers, microphones etc).

Fig 3.10 shows a WebSDR monitoring 20m. The small window marker at 14.155MHz marks the audio passband that is shown on the WSJT-X wide graph. This was taken using the speaker – microphone method discussed earlier and you can see some odd artefacts: the dark vertical stripes in the wide graph as a result. You can still see my FT8 signal on this graph, but it is quite weak. Using

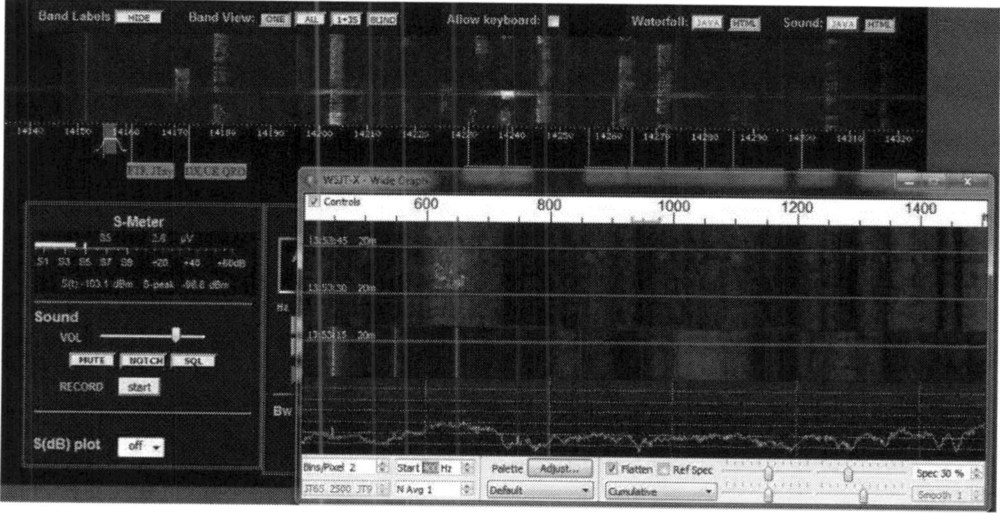

Fig 3.10: WebSDR showing spectrum scope and WSJT Wide Graph as an insert.

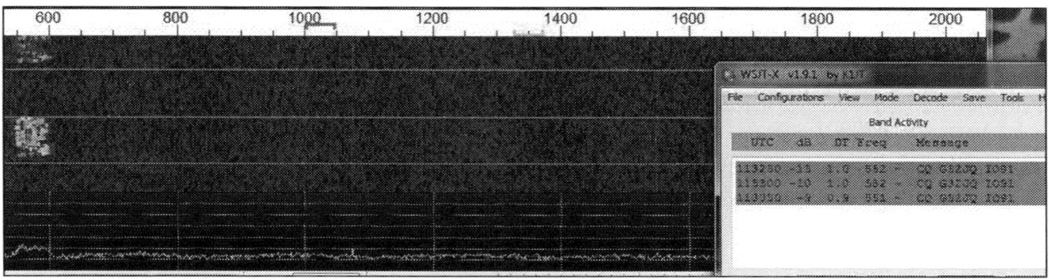

Fig 3.11: G3ZJQ's FT8 signal as received by a WebSDR.

the virtual cable to connect my web browser to WSJT-X directly results in a cleaner signal. This is shown in **Fig 3.11**. The absence of any harmonics is confirmation that the audio level has been set correctly.

Of the three methods to set the correct audio level, the sampling method is the most accurate and is recommended. However, using a WebSDR uses less equipment and does give you confidence that your signals are clean. You can use the setup procedure without monitoring, but this is a last resort and not recommended.

Finally, perhaps the easiest method is to get a friendly local FT8 operator to give you honest feedback on your signal when transmitting on a clear frequency away from the main FT8 'watering holes'.

Both WSJT-X and JTDX have a setting that minimises the transmission of harmonics and this is worth using. *Split operation* adjusts the transmit frequency to keep the FT8 tones between 1500Hz and 2000Hz so that any harmonics, which will be greater than 3000Hz, fall outside the passband of the normal SSB transceiver. There are two options to do this: using the transceiver's A and B VFOs or letting the program emulate this by shifting the transmit frequency.

For example, if you are transmitting at 550Hz on the waterfall and your transceiver is set to 14.074MHz, your actual transmit frequency will be 14.074550MHz and the potential second harmonic will be 1100Hz. Under split operation when WSJT-X or JTDX goes into transmit it will adjust the frequency on the transceiver to 14.073MHz and the FT8 tones to 1550Hz. The actual transmit frequency is still 14.074550MHz but now the second harmonic will be at 3100Hz which is above the passband and hence will be attenuated.

Split operation is set up under File –> Settings –> Radio in both programs. If you chose 'Rig', the program will use the VFO A / B method and switch between VFOs when you transmit. But make sure that you have set up both VFOs to data mode otherwise you may find yourself attempting to transmit on USB or even LSB!

Now the receive and transmit setup is complete, we can start making QSOs. Firstly, let's consider how to set the transmit frequency. The programs show you all the activity in a 3000Hz bandwidth and multiple stations can easily fit into this

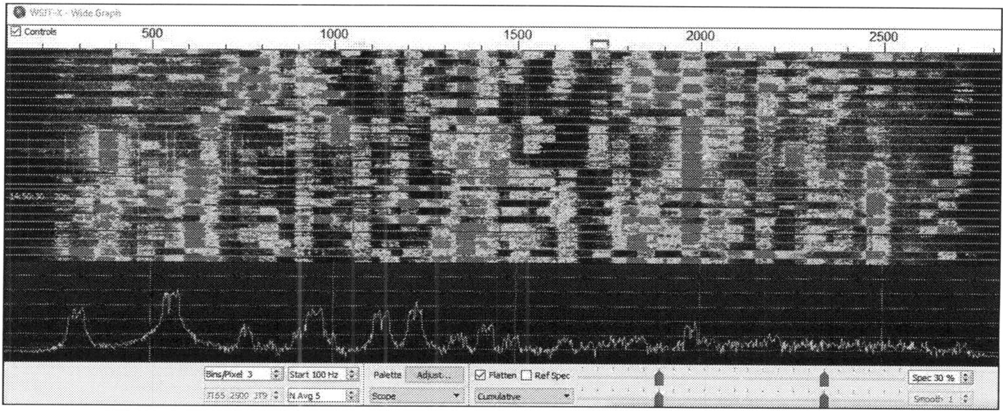

Fig 3.12: 20m at a busy time.

range, since FT8 only occupies 50Hz. On a typically busy day on most bands this can look crowded, **Fig 3.12**.

The aim is to choose a frequency that is clear; these are dark blue on the waterfall. It is not necessary or desirable to call a station on its own frequency since split frequency operation is preferable (note this is different from the split operation discussed earlier). It avoids the pile-up when a station calling CQ has multiple respondents calling him, each causing QRM to the others. However, the choice of transmit frequency can only be done by selecting a clear frequency at the transmitting station's end and this could cause QRM at the DX station's location or indeed elsewhere. The FT8 software is tolerant of overlapping stations and this helps in this situation.

Once you have chosen a clear frequency there are a few other settings that you might find useful before you start transmitting. **Fig 3.13** shows a part of the main screen that includes tick boxes for 'Auto Seq' (Auto Sequence), 'Call 1st' and 'Hold Tx Freq', Auto Sequence allows the program to transmit a series of standard messages that complete a QSO by exchanging callsigns, locators, signal strengths and finally a 73 message. Call 1st instructs WSJT to respond to

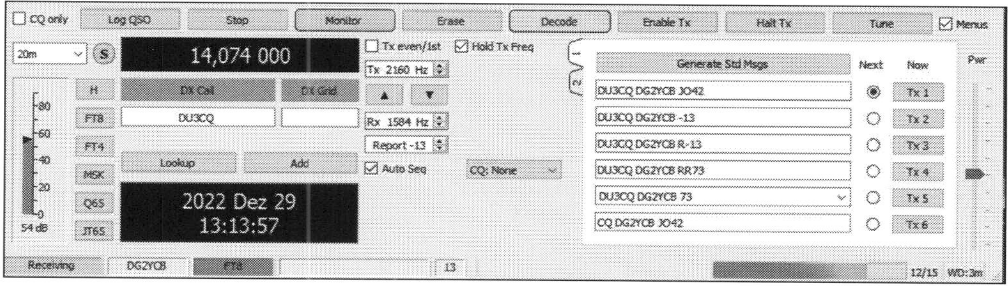

Fig 3.13: WSJT-X operating window (image: https://sourceforge.net/projects/wsjt/).

the first decoded reply to your CQ call. Hold Tx Frequency is self-explanatory and stops your transmit frequency from shifting as you respond to various stations (in JTDX this control is called 'Tx/Rx Split' and normally it should always be illuminated green).

You can alter the behaviour of WSJT-X in the File –> Settings –> General box as shown in **Fig 3.14**. It is convenient to let WSJT-X set the Tx Enable as well as populate the standard messages with the callsign of the station you are trying to contact when you double click on the station's message in the Band Activity window. This makes it easy to respond to a calling station. Similarly, it is also convenient to let the software disable the Tx after the contact is completed and almost essential to setup a prompt to yourself to log each contact.

Finally, it is useful to setup reporting across the internet, assuming that you have internet access from the computer running the software. **Fig 3.15** shows how you can do this by clicking on 'Enable PSK Reporter

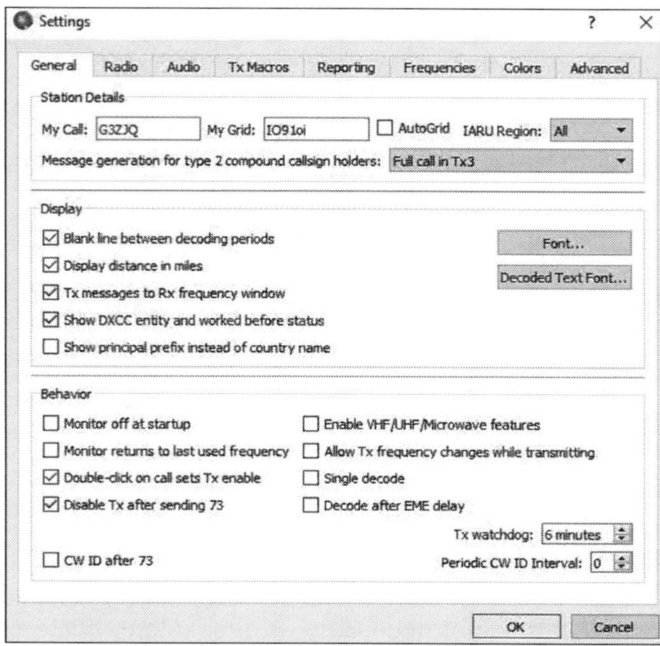

Fig 3.14: WSJT-X File –> Settings –> General box.

Fig 3.15: WSJT-X reporting and logging.

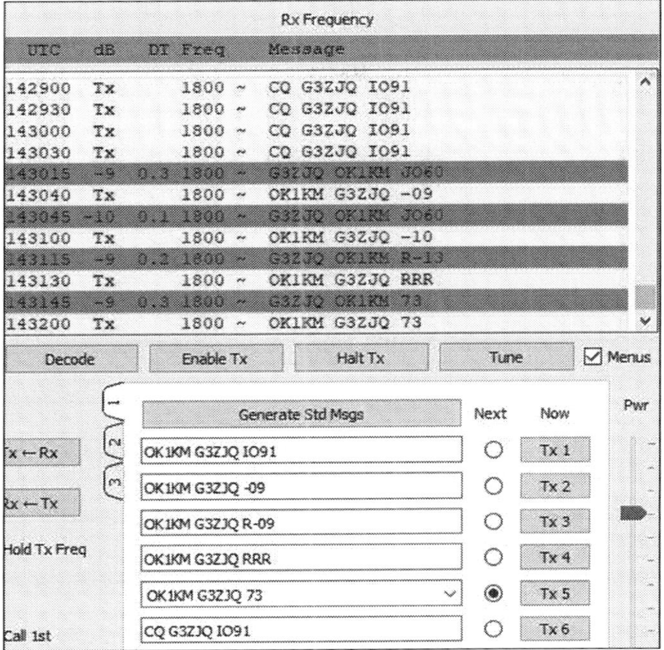

Fig 3.16: Originating a CQ call.

Rx Frequency

UTC	dB	DT	Freq		Message
131615	-9	0.1	1607	~	CQ HB9HVF JN47
131639	Tx		1607	~	HB9HVF G3ZJQ IO91
131645	-14	0.1	1607	~	CQ HB9HVF JN47
131700	Tx		1607	~	HB9HVF G3ZJQ IO91
131730	Tx		1607	~	HB9HVF G3ZJQ IO91
131800	Tx		1607	~	HB9HVF G3ZJQ IO91
131815	-5	0.1	1607	~	G3ZJQ HB9HVF -20
131845	1	0.1	1607	~	G3ZJQ HB9HVF -20
131904	Tx		1607	~	HB9HVF G3ZJQ IO91
131915	-3	0.1	1606	~	G3ZJQ HB9HVF -20
131930	Tx		1607	~	HB9HVF G3ZJQ R-03
131945	-2	0.1	1606	~	G3ZJQ HB9HVF RRR
132000	Tx		1607	~	HB9HVF G3ZJQ 73
132015	-2	0.1	1606	~	G3ZJQ HB9HVF 73
132230	-15	0.2	1616	~	BD3PXM VE1DBM FN85

Fig 3.17: Answering a CQ call.

Spotting' in the File –> Settings –> Reporting tab.

By now you should be eager to use the software and make a call, but first 'listen' to the band and make sure your intended transmit frequency is still unoccupied. If it is, click on the button box next to the CQ message, Tx 6, and enable the Tx. You should see your transceiver go to transmit in the next available time slot and the waterfall will freeze.

The CQ message is sent again after listening for a response and this will repeat until you either get a response, shown in red highlight in the Rx window, or you disable Tx enable. When you get a response, you just double click on it and the software will add the required information to the standard messages and begin the auto sequence. This whole process is shown in **Fig 3.16**.

Answering a CQ call (**Fig 3.17**) is just as simple. Check that your transmit frequency is still clear and just double click on the CQ message. The software will generate the standard messages, begin transmitting in the next time slot and complete the QSO automatically.

Having enjoyed several contacts or at least having sent CQ messages, you can monitor your performance using PSK Reporter found at **https://pskreporter.info/pskmap.html**.

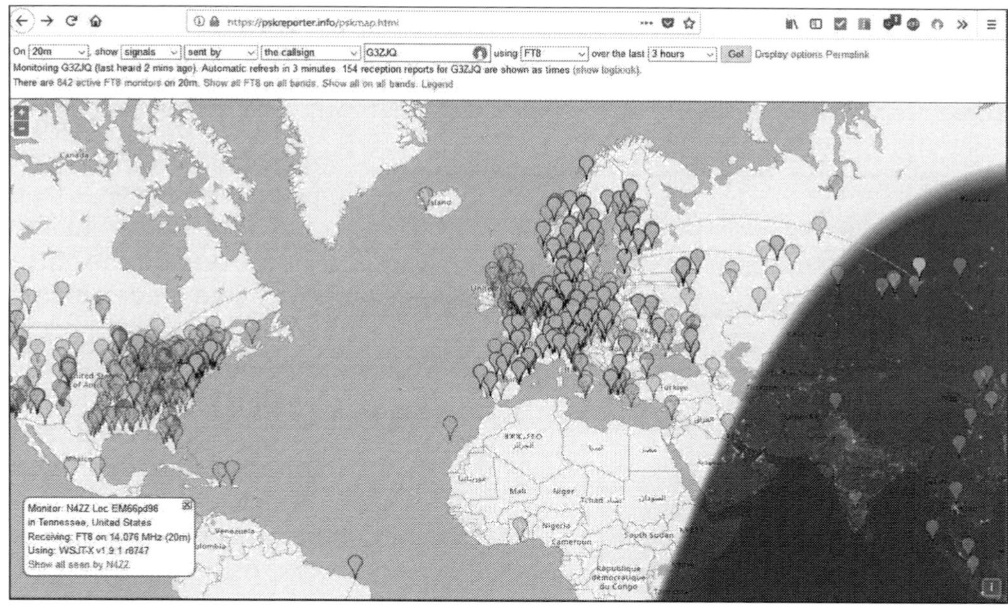

Fig 3.18: PSK Reporter map.

A typical map is shown in **Fig 3.18**. Each callout in **Fig 3.18** is a monitoring station. If you setup PSK Reporter Spotting previously, your own station will appear as one of these callouts. The lines connect your station to all those who have received your signals, so you can see at a glance how well your station is performing. If you rest your cursor on top of one of these monitors you will get some further information about the monitoring station and if this monitor has received your signal this will include a signal report. **Fig 3.19** shows such a report from PY2WND for G3ZJQ's 8-watt FT8 transmission using a half-size G5RV at 5 metres above ground level. FT8 is an excellent weak-signal mode!

So far we have discussed operating FT8 mode in a normal amateur QSO context, i.e. a one-to-one communication between amateurs. However, one of the big advantages of digital modes – and FT8 in particular – is their weak-signal capability and this makes them well adapted to DX operation. Even stations with relatively low power and modest

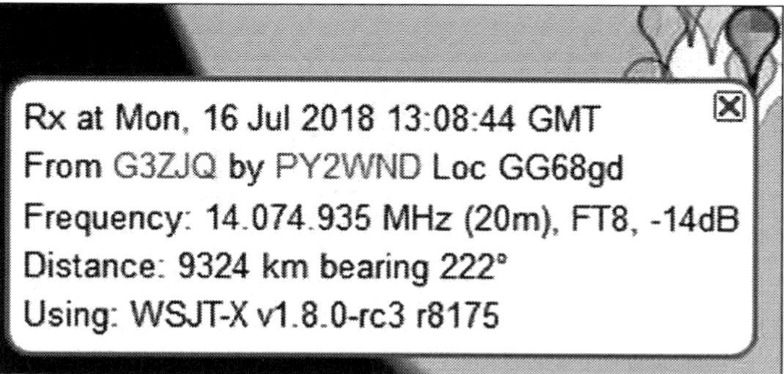

Fig 3.19: PSK Reporter signal report.

antennas can make significant DX contacts using FT8. This has a potential impact on both DXpeditions and contests. However, FT8 was originally not well suited to the requirements of DXpeditioning or contesting. An FT8 QSO takes several exchanges, each one of which takes 15 seconds (and sometimes repeats are required). This limits the QSO rate and can make operating with large pile-ups difficult to manage.

Furthermore the fixed message format of FT8 makes contest operating impossible if further information in addition to the callsign, report and locator is required. Version 2.0 of WSJT-X addressed both of these needs and these are discussed in the following sections.

FT8 DXPEDITION OPERATING MODE: 'FOX AND HOUNDS'

An FT8 operating mode, first introduced in WSJT-X 1.9, is intended for DXpedition use and is called 'Fox and Hounds' mode, often abbreviated 'F/H'. The aim is to allow the DXpedition (the 'Fox') to complete many more QSOs per hour with the calling stations (the 'Hounds') than the normal FT8 operating mode would allow. This is achieved by allocating the first 1000Hz of the FT8 waterfall exclusively to the remote DXpedition or Fox. The region between 1000Hz and 3000Hz (or greater) is where the Hounds call the Fox. By separating the two it allows the Fox to respond to several calling stations simultaneously during each 15-second time slot and hence improve the QSO rate. The operating sequence is partly automated and follows the following stages:

1. The Fox calls CQ within the 300 – 900Hz region.
2. Several Hounds respond in the next time slot using frequencies *above* 1000Hz.
3. The Fox responds with signal reports to each station, again within the 300 – 900Hz region.
4. Each Hound completes the exchange by giving the Fox his report *on the same frequency upon which he was called* by the Fox. This frequency shift is controlled by the software.
5. The Fox completes each QSO with an RR73 message.

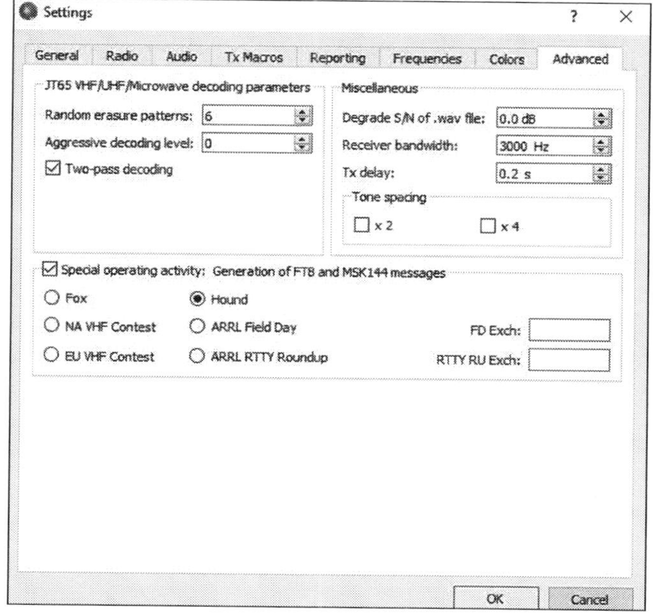

Fig 3.20: Setting up Fox and Hounds mode.

To operate as a Hound you will need to set up CAT control of your transceiver, split frequency operation (both these setting can be found in File –> Settings –> Radio), check Monitor returns to last used frequency (File –>Settings –> General) and select Hound in the Special Activities subsection of File –> Settings –> Advanced: see **Fig 3.20**. Version 2.6 of WSJT-X now provides a new button on the main window allowing FT8 'Hound' mode to be toggled on and off. In JTDX it is simply a matter of clicking the main screen's 'Hound' button.

Since operating as a Hound is quite different to the normal FT8 QSO you should not attempt to contact the Fox using the standard FT8 mode. It is worth noting that the default Hound mode does not decode signals above 1000Hz but they are still visible on the waterfall so that you can find a clear frequency. If you want to monitor the pile-up you can decode all received signals by checking the Rx All Freq box on the main window (WSJT-X). Some options used in the standard mode will disappear from the main window when in Hound mode and a bright red box indicating Hound mode will appear (WSJT-X).

Good operating practice is not to call the Fox:

1. If you cannot hear him [that should go without saying – *Ed*]; or
2. If the Fox is calling using a directed CQ and you are not within that continent.

To call the Fox you double click his decoded message. A typical exchange is shown in **Table 3.2**. The Fox, 5R8PA in this example, calls CQ (Tx 6) and several stations respond (their Tx 1). In his next transmission the Fox completes a QSO with HL5OC (who had called previously) and, simultaneously, responds to two of the new callers, BA3WW and IU0HDC, by sending their reports. Those

	FOX'S TRANSMISSIONS	HOUNDS' TRANSMISSIONS
Tx 6	CQ 5R8PA LH46	
Tx 1		5R8PA BA3WW OM67
Tx 1		5R8PA IU0HDC JN62
Tx 1		5R8PA PJ4DX FK52
		etc
Tx 2	HL5OC 5R8PA RR73	
Tx 2	BA3WW 5R8PA –04	
Tx 2	IU0HDC 5R8PA –12	
Tx 3		5R8PA BA3WW R–05
Tx 3		5R8PA IU0HDC R–10
Tx 1		5R8PA PJ4DX FK52
		etc
Tx 4	BA3WW 5R8PA RR73	
Tx 4	IU0HDC 5R8PA RR73	
Tx 4	PJ4DX 5R8PA –10	

Table 3.2: Sequence of events in Fox and Hounds QSO exchanges.

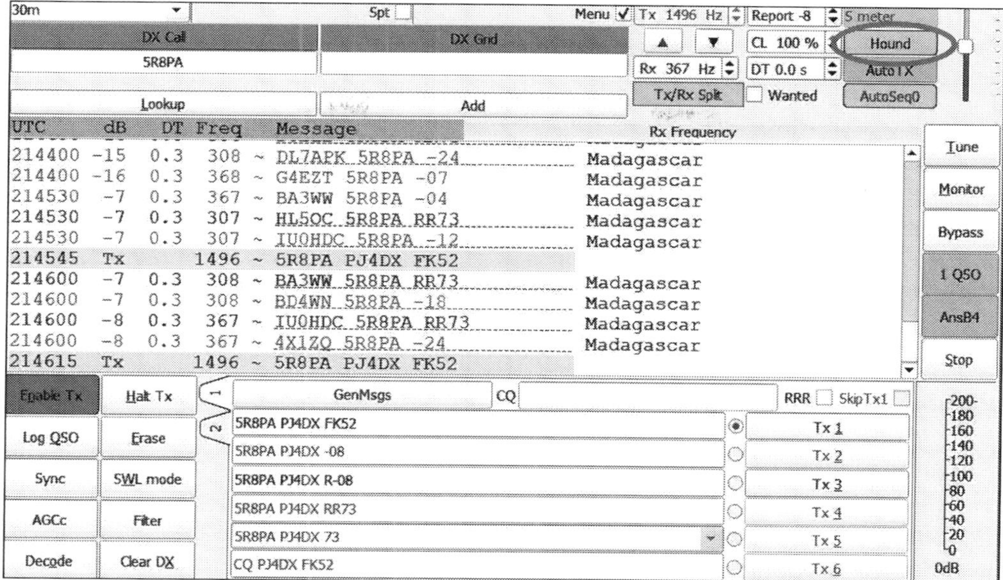

Fig 3.21: Operating as a 'Hound' using the JTDX program.

stations then send their report to the Fox and, at the same time, PJ4DX makes his initial (Tx 1) call to the Fox, by sending his Grid. The Fox then confirms the QSOs with BA3WW and IU0HDC by sending RR73 messages and sends a signal report to PJ4DX in the same time slot.

This sequence of events is actually a real-life example of contacts that took place using Fox and Hounds mode on 30m FT8 in November 2022. It is shown in **Fig 3.21**. 5R8PA was running four or five streams and it can be seen that at 2146:00 he completed QSOs with BA3WW and IU0HDC by sending them 'RR73' messages while, at the same time, sending initial reports of –18dB and –24dB respectively to BD4WN and 4X1ZO. Your editor, PJ4DX, completed the QSO with 5R8PA immediately after!

Note that **Fig 3.21** shows the JTDX screen, rather than that of WSJT-X. With all versions of JTDX up to and including the current version (January 2023) it is *not* possible to operate as a Fox, though JTDX users can *call* Foxes simply by clicking on the 'Hound' button (circled in **Fig 3.21**) and setting the Tx frequency above 1000Hz as described above (in fact JTDX will not *allow* you to call a Fox if you have clicked the 'Hound' button and attempt to set your frequency below 1000Hz, a useful 'sanity check'!)

The ability of the Fox to send multiple messages within the same time slot increases the QSO rate over the standard mode. There are no RRR or 73 messages from the Hound and this also helps to keep the QSO rate high.

Transmitting as the Fox is slightly more complex since there are more things to manage. WSJT-X has several features in Fox mode that help the operator to manage the pile-up:

The left hand pane on the main window becomes a Stations Calling Fox window which can be sorted by distance, signal strength, time (age) etc; there is an additional log window, and the number of simultaneous transmissions can be increased, allowing the Fox to respond to several stations at the same time. Several new features were introduced in WSJT-X version 2.6. A table provides an overview of the queue of stations calling and of callsigns with QSOs in progress. The Fox operator can change the ordering of callsigns in the queue, allowing the operator to react to changes in propagation. The Fox now responds automatically for another two cycles to stations whose report has not been received, increasing the success rate for difficult QSOs.

More details about the WSJT-X DXpedition mode can be found at: **https://wsjt.sourceforge.io/FT8_DXpedition_Mode.pdf**

The MSHV program, described briefly on pages 23 – 24, does not include Fox and Hounds, but it *does* allow for multi-streaming when in DX mode. MSHV allows the DX station to respond to up to 10 callers simultaneously, thus increasing the rate of making contacts many fold. The available transmitter power is divided between all the streams so, unless signal strengths are high, it is possible the DX station may not be received if too many streams are attempted.

If the DX station is using MSHV multi-streaming it is not necessary to call as a Hound, or to call above 1000Hz. However, for the receiving station it can often be difficult to determine whether a DXpedition is using WSJT-X Fox and Hounds or MSHV multi-streaming. One clue is that F/H mode Foxes *always* transmit in the 1st (00/30) Tx period, so if a multi-streaming DX station is transmitting in the 2nd (15/45) period by definition they *must* be using MSHV.

If the calling station is still unclear which program is being used by the DX station, *if using JTDX* it is safer to call above 1000Hz as a ‘Hound’ because if the DX station is using MSHV, the QSO *can* still be completed. On the other hand, if the DX station is using WSJT-X F/H and the calling station does *not* call as a Hound his signal will not be received and so no QSO can take place. If the *receiving* station is using WSJT-X, though, calling as a Hound automatically causes them to transmit in the 2nd period: clearly if the DX station is *also* transmitting in the 2nd period it won’t be possible to make a contact. It therefore makes sense to spend some time to determine which program the DX station is using, rather than just calling ‘blind’.

FT8 CONTEST MODES

New FT8 protocols allow more information to be passed in each exchange and this has made FT8 more contest friendly:

- NA VHF Contest mode allows for /R callsigns;
- EU VHF Contest mode allows for /P callsigns;
- ARRL Field Day mode allows for the exchange of Field Day operating classes required by the contest rules. This information is entered into the FD Each: box found on the File –> Settings –> Advanced page;

- ARRL RTTY roundup mode is similar to the Field Day mode and exchanges the required signal report (RST) and State.

These modes can be setup on the Special Activities section of the File –> Settings –> Advanced page in WSJT-X in a similar manner to the Fox and Hounds mode discussed above.

One of the enhancements of WSJT-X version 2.6, released in January 2023, was the implementation of new features supporting the ARRL International Digital Contest, with its distance-based scoring. The 'Call 1st' box has been replaced by a drop-down control offering 'CQ Max Dist' as an alternative. A new window labelled 'Active Stations' displays a list of received but unworked callsigns, sorted in decreasing order of potential contest points. With the 'CQ Max Dist' option selected, the program will select the reply to your CQ that yields the most contest points. You can then click on a line in the 'Active Stations' window to call that station.

FT4 FOR CONTESTING AND DXING

FT4 was designed especially for contesting and was introduced in WSJT-X version 2.1 in 2019. It is now used for DXing and indeed general day-to-day operating as well as for contesting. Both JTDX and MSHV also include FT4 in their packages and **Fig 3.22** shows FT4 in operation (outside a contest period). The FT4 tones are 90Hz wide, compared with just 50Hz for FT8. FT4 is a similar protocol to FT8, but it is twice as fast, with 7.5-second transmit and receive periods rather than the 15-second periods of FT8. Other than the differences to the timing of the periods the user interface is almost identical to that of FT8. The additional speed comes at the expense of about 3.5dB in sensitivity, but when

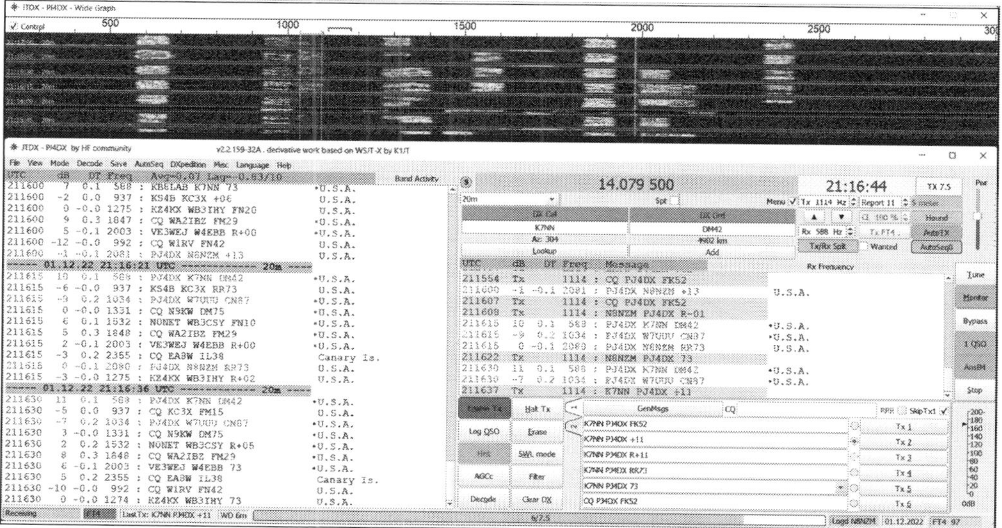

Fig 3.22: FT4 main screen and waterfall display.

signals are strong this hardly matters as, generally, very nearly as many stations can be decoded.

In **Fig 3.22** the waterfall display is shown above the main operating screen, which is how it might normally be configured. It can be seen that the tones and the transmit and receive cursors on the waterfall display are wider than the corresponding ones in FT8, while the horizontal lines separating the time periods are closer together, compared with those of FT8.

Although originally intended for contesting, the fact that FT4 is so much faster than FT8 has also led to it being used by DXpeditions in order to work more stations in the time available. Due to the high band noise and / or weak signals expected, some DXpeditions use FT8 on 1.8, 3.5 and 50MHz, and FT4 on the bands in between, where it can be assumed that the signal-to-noise ratio will be greater. FT4 is also used by resident DX operators, who often find they have many stations calling them simultaneously when using FT8, and so they move to FT4 to increase their rate of making contacts.

The RSGB has been keen to promote the use of FT4 for contest operating and organises a series of short-duration (90-minute) FT4 contests that take place in the 80, 40 and 20 metre bands between 8.00pm and 9.30pm UK local time, nine times a year.

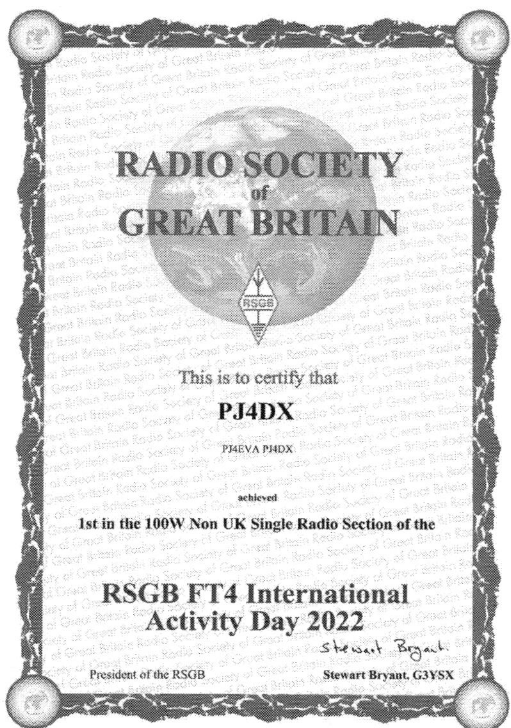

Fig 3.23: RSGB FT4 International Activity Day contest certificate.

The RSGB also organises an annual 24-hour FT4 'International Activity Day' in April in the 160, 80, 40, 20, 15 and 10m bands. Taking part with his wife Eva, PJ4EVA, the editor of this book participated in the inaugural FT4 International Activity Day in 2022 and won the 100W Non-UK section of the contest, **Fig 3.23**.

In both of these RSGB contests there are separate sections for power levels of up to 10 watts and up to 100 watts as well as for entrants in the UK and overseas. See **rsgbcc.org/hf** for full details of all RSGB HF contests including those on digi modes.

The main international contest using FT4 is the World Wide Digi DX Contest, which is held at the end of August each year. This is a 24-hour event taking place in the 160, 80, 40, 20, 15 and 10m bands and both FT4 *and* FT8 can be used. The full rules are at: **https://ww-digi.com/rules**

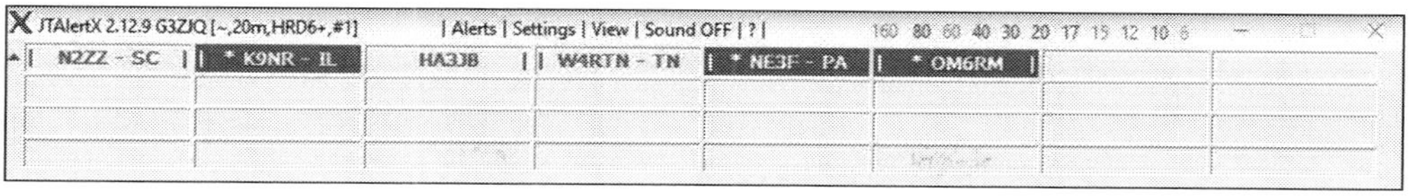

Fig 3.24: JTAlert Main window.

JTALERT

WSJT-X and the other programs are very powerful but there are some operating areas that they do not cover and there are other programs that can be used to fill in the gaps. One of the most popular is ***JTAlert***. It provides several operating aids, including audio and visual alerts that track wanted DXCC entities, prefixes and grid squares, as well as automatic logging to several online logging programs. This program by Laurie Cowcher, VK3AMA, is a free download available from: **http://hamapps.com**. It is only available for the Windows platform. The installation is easy using a standard setup file. You need to start your weak-signal program first and then start JTAlert. Its main window is shown in **Fig 3.24**.

If you are receiving and decoding stations, after each decode period the stations heard will populate the spreadsheet like boxes in the main JTAlert window. **Fig 3.24** shows six active stations.

The alerts are colour coded and, in this case, the three stations in the darker boxes are calling CQ. The plain boxes contain stations that have no alert status and are just exchanging QSO information. By double-clicking on the box, you can initiate a reply to that station just the same as if you were to double-click on the station within WSJT-X, JTDX or MSHV. There are many more alert types available as can be seen in **Fig 3.25**. Each alert is colour coded and these colours can be changed in the Alert types page as shown in **Fig 3.26**.

Because JTAlert has many alerts it can quickly become confusing, so only turn on the alerts you find useful. The decode period for FT8 is only 15 seconds and, on a

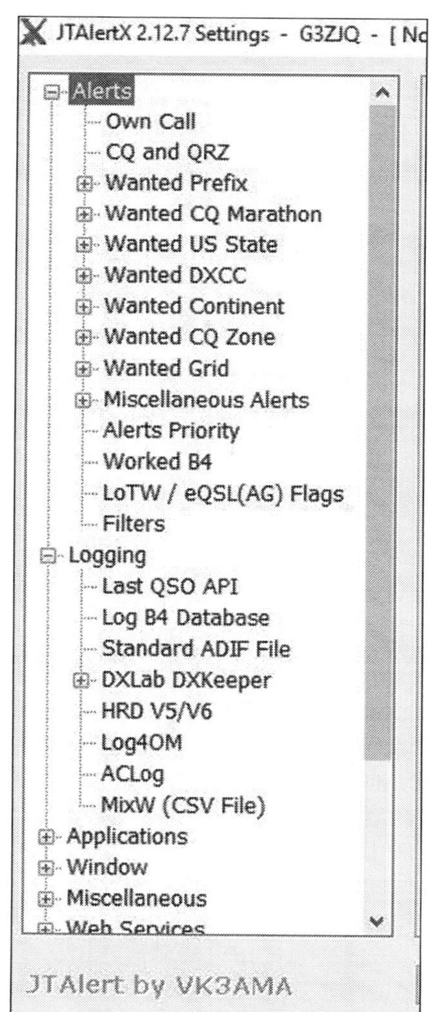

Fig 3.25: JTAlert settings.

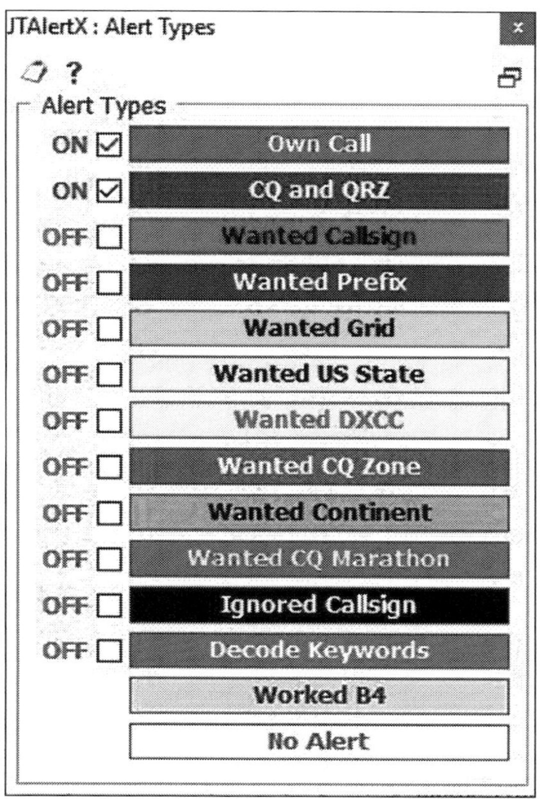

Fig 3.26: JTAlert alert types.

Fig 3.27: JTAlert boxes.

busy band, you can easily have 50 or more active stations, so these alerts can flash by very quickly.

You can set an alert priority so that stations triggering several alerts will only show the colour of the highest priority alert. One alert that is very useful is the CQ alert, which has the default colour green but it is also indicated by a "*" character in front of the callsign (the hash character "#" indicates a directed CQ). If you use these alert indicators, rather than the colour alert, you can combine the CQ alert with another alert, for example Wanted DXCC. It is then clear if the station calling CQ is on your wanted list: for example see LZ532PSO in **Fig 3.27** which shows a wanted DXCC calling CQ.

Two other pieces of information are also shown by symbols rather than colours: participation in Logbook of The World (LoTW) and membership of eQSL. LoTW participation is shown by a vertical stripe on the left of the box whilst eQSL is shown by a stripe on the right: see EW8W in **Fig 3.27**.

You can also setup audio alerts using .wav files that can be downloaded from the same site as the main program. If you wish to use audio alerts, make sure you set a different audio output device from the one used by WSJT-X, JTDX or MSHV, otherwise your alerts will be sent to your transceiver rather than your speakers! The audio output device is set in JTAlert via Settings –> Sound Card.

JTAlert does more than just offer alerts, it also has a band monitor that indicates the number of active JT65, JT9, and FT8 stations on all of the bands between 160m and 6m, **Fig 3.28**. It can be made visible by selecting it in the View tab on the main window. This information is also found as a single row of coloured band reference numbers found at the top right of the main JTAlert window, see **Fig 3.24**. The colour code can be customised in Settings –> Windows –> Band Activity Reports.

Band Activity

Unique Callsigns TX/RX per Band

Solar : SFI 71 : A 3 : K 1

	tx	rx	tx	rx	tx	rx		tx	rx	tx	rx	tx	rx
160m					76	26	17m					155	140
80m					220	104	15m					81	50
60m					69	48	12m						
40m	9	4	2	1	561	329	10m					6	6
30m					352	173	6m					35	11
20m	1	1			468	391	ALL	10	5	2	1	+1K	+1K

JT65 JT9 (Last Update : 23-Dec, 17:18 utc) FT8

Fig 3.28: JTAlert Band monitor.

Another useful feature of JTAlert is automated QSO logging. It is capable of working with several commonly-used logging programs: DXKeeper, HRD, Log4OM and ACLog. It also allows automatic links to several online logbooks: HRDLog.net and eQSL.cc, see **Fig 3.29**.

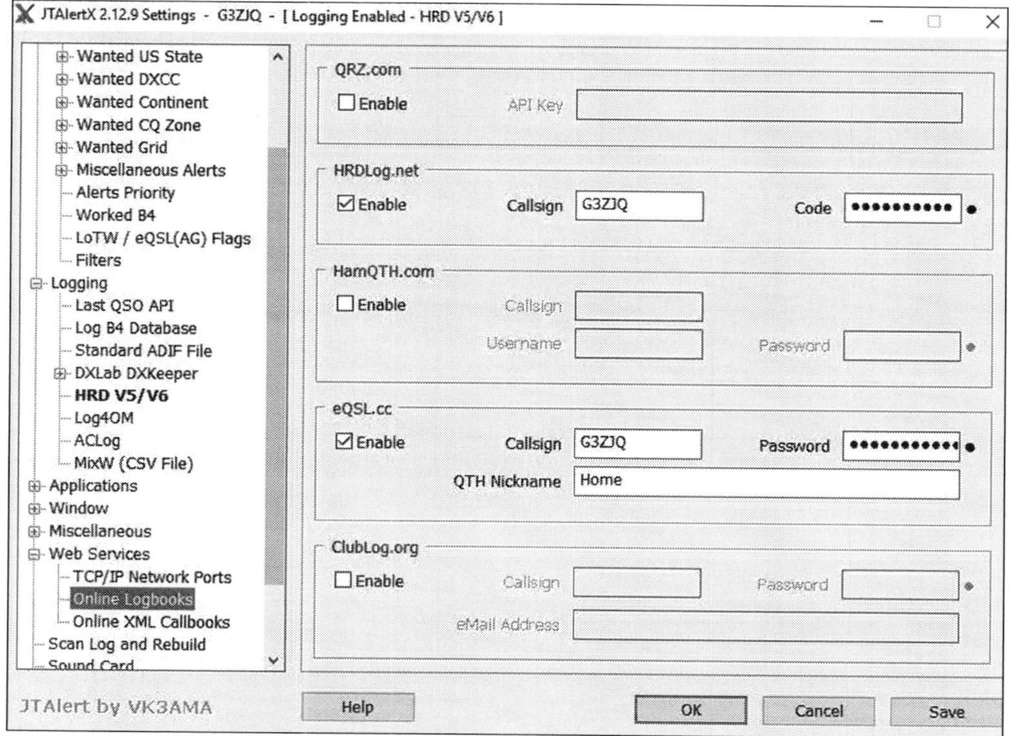

Fig 3.29: JTAlert logging options.

More details of these logging options can be found online using a simple search. More support for JTAlert can be found at: **https://hamapps.groups.io/g/Support**

GRID TRACKER

Grid Tracker is another cooperating program which allows the operator to track the grids, DXCC entities and also US counties contacted on FT8 and FT4. It was developed by Stephen 'Tag' Loomis, N0TTL, and Henry Forte, N2VFL. The latest Windows version (as of January 2023) is 1.23.0110 which can be downloaded free of charge from **https://gridtracker.org/**. There are also versions for MacOS and Linux.

Grid Tracker works with WSJT-X, JTDX and MSHV. It produces a list of all stations heard, highlighting the ones that the operator has indicated that he is interested in. Colour coding is used to differentiate between grids, US counties

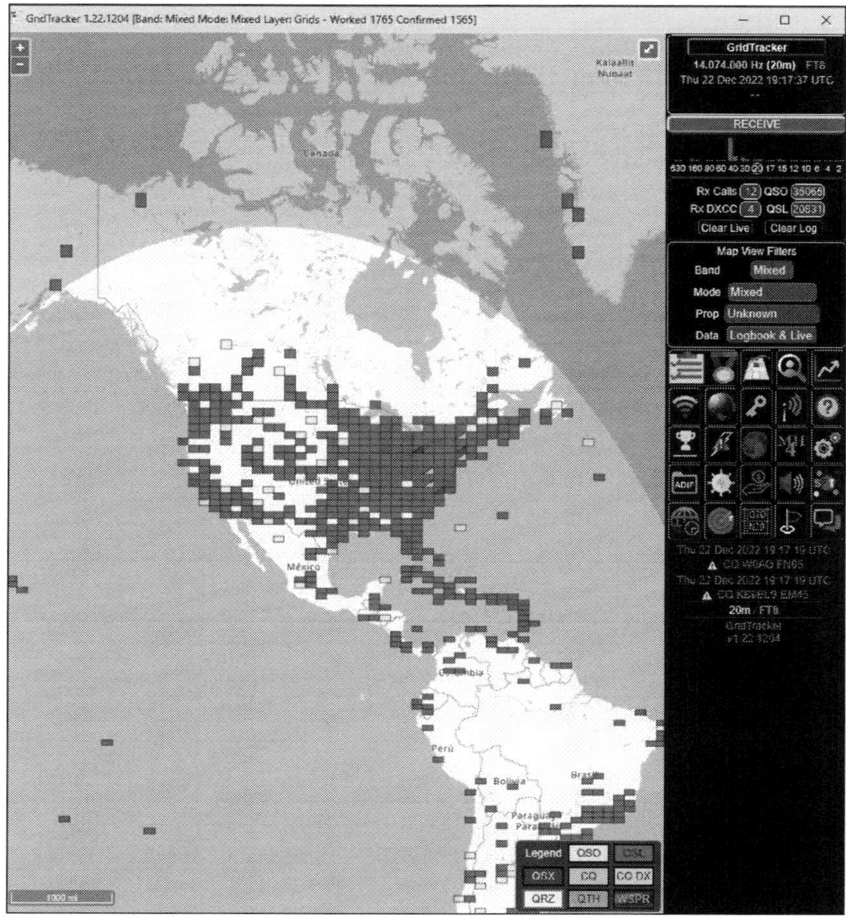

Fig 3.30: Grid Tracker map display showing Grids worked.

and DXCC entities and a customisable audio or visual alert informs the operator when a 'new one' is decoded or worked.

The program has a map display which shows grids worked, **Fig 3.30**, There are many map overlays and the maps can be moved to the particular area of interest or as the greyline moves across the world during the course of the day or night.

Fig 3.31 shows the working screen which refreshes with every cycle of FT8 or FT4, providing an instant up-to-date picture at the operator's fingertips. Right-clicking allows the grid columns to be setup to suit the operator's own requirements.

Grid Tracker integrates with several of the popular logging programs allowing the operator to keep track of their progress towards various awards.

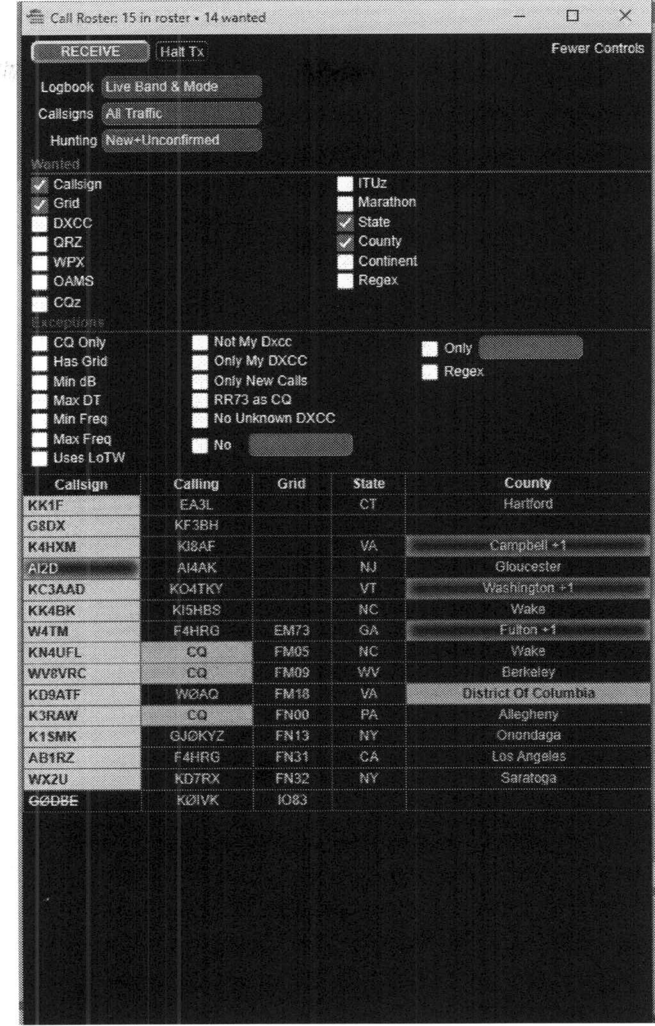

Fig 3.31: Working screen (images: Tom Wylie, GM4FDM / *CDXC Digest* 'FT Column').

USING FLDIGI IN BPSK31 MODE

Having completed the basic Fldigi configuration, you can explore the many different modes. Let's use BPSK31 as an example. If you have followed the previous chapter on setting up Fldigi and you are tuned to an active PSK frequency the waterfall should look like **Fig 3.32**.

Note that all of the signals that you can see will not necessarily be of BPSK31 signals and you must get used to identifying the mode from either the sound or the shape of the signal shown in the waterfall: BPSK31 is shown in **Fig 3.33**.

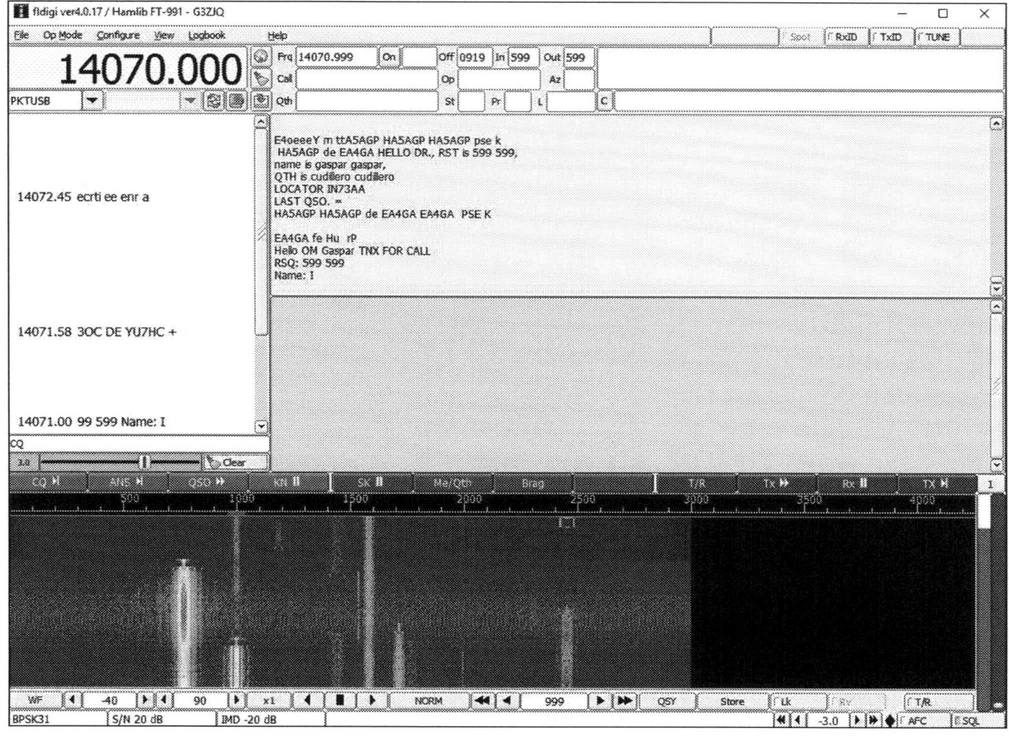

Fig 3.32: Fldigi in operation.

It can take some experimentation to get the mode right, but you will quickly get to recognise the various modes. Fldigi calls the various decoders modems and provides you with the ability to alter the modem parameters though it is best to leave these alone until you have gained more experience and knowledge.

The next stage is to adjust the Tx audio level to avoid overdriving your transceiver. This is done in a similar way to the setup described for WSJT-X and, if you have already setup the Tx audio level for WSJT-X, it will be easier to set up Fldigi.

Adjust the audio output level (speakers) on the sound card to midrange. In Windows 10 the level control is found in the same place as the microphone level adjustment explained earlier. Then adjust the mic or, if using the rear input, the data input level on your transceiver so that your signal is clean. On some transceivers this can be done whilst watching the ALC level and adjusting the drive to the point just before the ALC comes into effect. However,

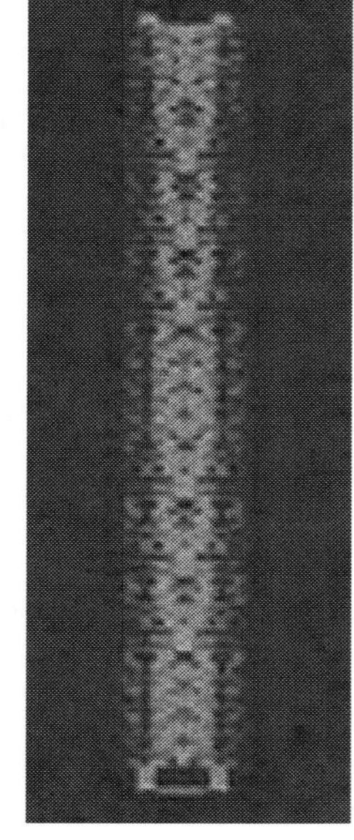

Fig 3.33: BPSK31 as it appears in the waterfall.

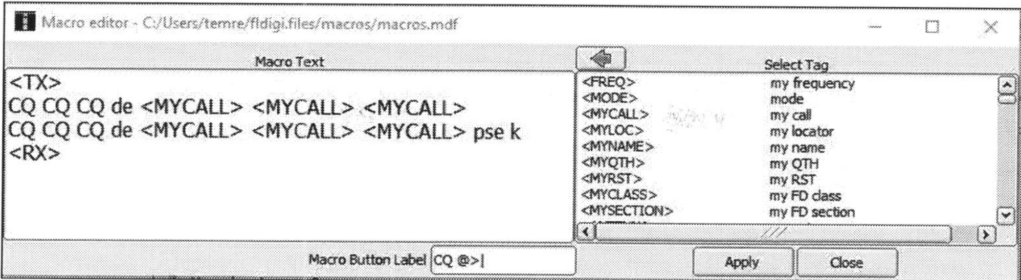

Fig 3.34: Macro editor.

a more accurate method is to get a friendly local BPSK31 operator to give you honest feedback on your signal when transmitting on a clear frequency away from the BPSK31 'watering holes'.

Another alternative is to monitor your own transmission using a WebSDR as you make the adjustments. Fldigi does offer an intermodulation distortion measurement of incoming signals as well as the signal-to-noise ratio so you may be able to get an IMD report from another station.

If you type a message into the transmit window and toggle the Tx button, your transceiver will transmit and send the message on the frequency indicated by the red lines on the waterfall. It will not return to receive automatically so you must toggle back to receive using either the T/R button, found on the command ribbon just above the waterfall, or by using the Pause / Break key on your keyboard.

On this command ribbon, you can find several macro keys. These will send defined text to the transmit window allowing you to send predetermined messages or parts of messages. For example, CQ is a standard message: "CQ CQ CQ de G3ZJQ G3ZJQ G3ZJQ CQ CQ CQ G3ZJQ G3ZJQ G3ZJQ pse k". If you right click the macro button it opens the macro editor with the macro loaded ready to be edited, **Fig 3.34**.

There are a number of set commands and parameters that you can use to create standard messages: <TX> acts like the PTT and turns on transmit and hence will send the following message without any further intervention, <MYCALL> is the callsign entered in the operator setup page, and finally <RX> will return to receive status. You can change the Macro Button Label to something you find more relevant, so you are not limited to the default ones. You can enter the information concerning the station you are contacting in the boxes at the top right, **Fig 3.35**.

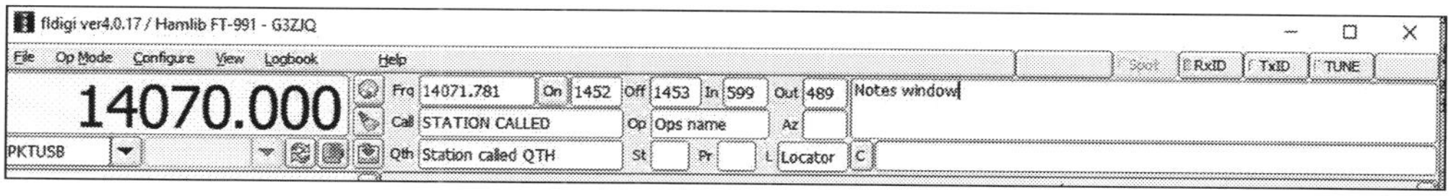

Fig 3.35: Entering the details of the station you are working.

If you enter the callsign and name of the person you are working, you can have these details automatically entered into any macro that uses the parameters <CALL> and <NAME>. You can also send the SN value in dB and the IMD automatically using <INFO1> and <INFO2> parameters in your macro. The RST signal report is <RST> and needs to be entered in the Out box next to the notes window, see **Fig 3.35**. There are four sets of 12 macros to choose between.

Finally, there are some keyboard commands worth noting: ESC will abort the current transmission and end it with an appropriate post amble, whereas hitting ESC three times will end the current transmission abruptly.

To select a frequency or respond to a CQ call you just click on the channel displayed in the Browser window and the red lines will jump to the appropriate frequency in the waterfall. The signal will be decoded and presented in both the Browser window and the Receive window. If you are not tuned to a valid BPSK31 signal you will just see random letters appear on both of these windows.

Just as with WSJT-X, you can link Fldigi to PSK reporter by ticking the boxes under Configure –> Miscellaneous –> PSK Reporter.

TIPS FOR USING BPSK31

The following tips for using BPSK31 are edited from a longer piece written back in 2008 and published on the ARRL website.

- Use the centre of your waterfall display whenever you can, since it offers the best Tx power and Rx capability.
- Minimise the use of UPPER case letters. Lower case letters use fewer bits (see the later discussion of varicodes).
- Use your transceiver's RF gain control or attenuator to avoid being desensitised by very strong signals.
- Keep your ALC reading as close to zero as possible.
- Remember, BPSK31 has an 80% duty cycle, so keep the power down to protect your equipment.

See **http://www.arrl.org/news/10-tips-for-the-psk31-digital-mode** for the complete article..

SUMMARY

In this chapter we covered digital mode operating using FT8 and BPSK31 as example modes. Both DX operating using WSJT-X Fox and Hounds mode and the MSHV multi-streaming DX mode, and contest activity using FT4 and FT8, were also covered. Several software packages were discussed, WSJT-X and Fldigi in detail, including the important topic of setting up the audio Tx drive levels to avoid generating harmonics.

4. Keyboard Modes: JS8 and VarAC

In this book we have covered setting up a digital station, operating using HF digital modes and we have explored the underlying technologies that give these modes their high performance. We have used several software packages, including WSJT-X, JTDX and Fldigi, to illustrate the setup procedures and we discussed operational techniques of FT8, FT4 and PSK31.

HF digital has become very popular in recent times. It offers better performance than SSB and even CW yet, despite this, there are some who feel that the automated text responses in modes such as FT8 and FT4 are not in the 'spirit' of amateur radio.

Joe Taylor, K1JT, updated FT8 in WSJT-X version 2.0 and introduced FT4 to include more features that are of interest to the contesting and DXing community. The upgrade demonstrated that interest in weak-signal modes is increasing and finding application outside of the technical domain and into mainstream amateur operating. Now, in 2023, there are more HF contacts made on FT8 than on all other modes combined (including CW and SSB)!

However, the 'keyboard' modes such as PSK31 have developed more slowly. There has been some development in the modulation techniques used, moving from BPSK31 to other PSK modes that have more bits per symbol, such as QPSK. More recently, keyboard modes such as JS8 and VarAC have been developed and we will take a look at these in more detail.

JS8 AND JS8CALL

JS8 is an experimental keyboard mode based on the FT8 protocol and originally developed in 2017 by Jordan Sherer, KN4CRD. The first public release of JS8Call version 1.0, **Fig 4.1**, was released in 2019 by Mark Bumstead, M0IAX, and the latest version (as of January 2023) is 2.2.0, which came out in June 2020. The software is available for Windows, Mac OSX, Linux 32 and 64-bit, and Rasp-

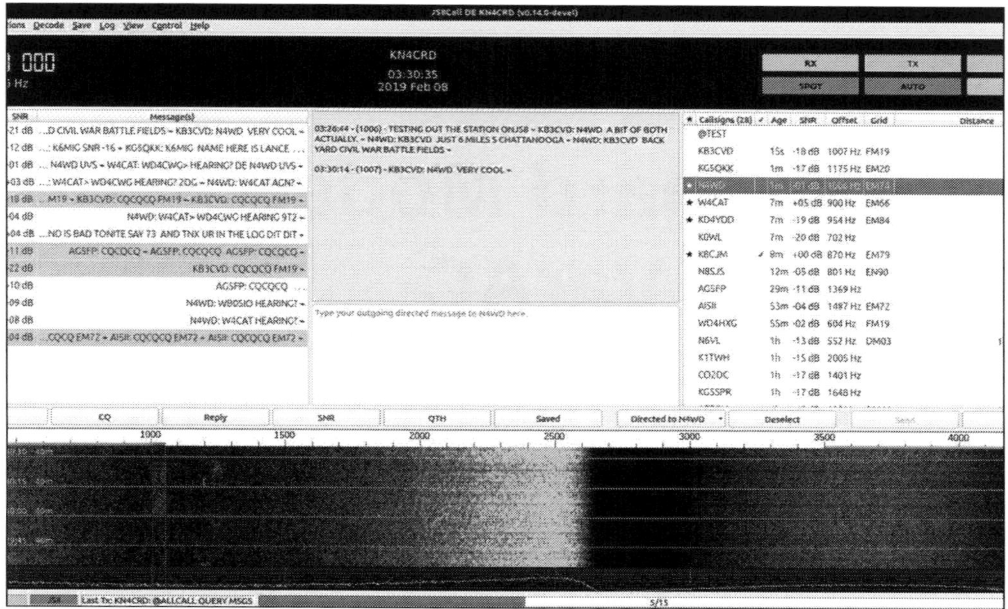

Fig 4.1: JS8Call version 1.0 (image: http://js8call.com)

berry Pi operating systems and it is available as a free dpwnload from **http://js8call.com**. There is also an official JS8Call Group for the development, testing and discussion of the mode at **https://groups.io/g/js8call**.

The js8call.com website states: "JS8Call is an *experiment* to test the feasibility of a digital mode with the robustness of FT8, combined with a messaging and network protocol layer for weak signal *communication* on HF, using a keyboard messaging style interface. It is not designed for any specific purpose other than connecting amateur radio operators who are operating under weak signal conditions. JS8Call is heavily inspired by WSJT-X, Fldigi, and FSQCall and would not exist without the hard work and dedication of the many developers in the amateur radio community.

"JS8Call uses a custom FT8 modulation called JS8 (Jordan Sherer designed 8-FSK modulation). This is the base RF transport. JS8Call has a 'directed calling' protocol laid over [the] top [of] the base RF transport to support free-form and directed message passing. Hence JS8 + Directed Calling = JS8Call." (Note that the app is named JS8Call, while the mode is JS8.)

Since JS8Call is based upon WSJT-X, you will find setting up this software, interface and your transceiver easy. In fact, once installed, the software just needs your callsign and locator to be entered together with the audio devices you are using for digital modes. Your transceiver might not need any adjustment at all but it is worth checking the power levels, just in case! The main HF and 6m frequencies used for JS8 can be found in **Table 3.1** on page 30.

As you would expect, operating using JS8Call is quite different to operating using FT8. To allow free format text, JS8 uses different source coding to FT8, so the two modes are not compatible with each other. The JS8 protocol breaks your text message down into 23 character blocks that it sends in back-to-back 15-second time slots using the FT8 error-correction techniques, so it may take several minutes to send and receive even a short sentence. Nets and group communications are featured in JS8Call, including a novel feature that sends a message that all listening stations will automatically respond to, giving you a signal report.

JS8Call is built upon the WSJT-X code base, which is only possible because WSJT-X is open-source software distributed under the GNU General Public License. The source code is freely available from SourceForge.net and the software tools needed to modify, compile and test the software are also freely available online. This makes it possible for anyone with the required skills to produce derivative software in a similar manner to constructing hardware to published designs, only cheaper. It is not necessary to do a complete project on your own, you can also contribute to the existing development teams.

Version 2.0 of JS8Call introduced two new faster mode speeds for QSOs, while version 2.1 introduced a slow mode. The four speeds available in JS8 are:

- Slow: 30 second frames, 25Hz bandwidth, around 8WPM, decoded down to –28dB;
- Normal: 15 second frames, 50Hz bandwidth, around 16WPM, decoded down to –24dB;
- Fast: 10 second frames, 80Hz bandwidth, around 24WPM, decoded down to –20dB;
- Turbo: 6 second frames, 160Hz bandwidth, around 40WPM, decoded down to –18dB.

According to the JS8Call website, the intent of the faster speeds is to start the QSO as normal and 'upgrade' to faster speeds if conditions are good enough to support it. "If you have a modern PC with a performant CPU, you can optionally enable MULTI from the mode menu, allowing the decoder to decode all mode speeds at once."

VARAC

VarAC – Introduction

As has been noted, some of the most popular data modes, including FT8 and FT4, restrict the QSO exchange to the minimum of information. Whilst this is fine for making marginal contacts, it lacks the personal element and leaves no opportunity to create new friendships and share your radio interest with others. VarAC has been specifically developed to buck the trend and provide a mode optimised for keyboard-to-keyboard chatting. Whilst we do have other modes available such as RTTY, PSK31, Olivia etc, we can do much more with today's technology.

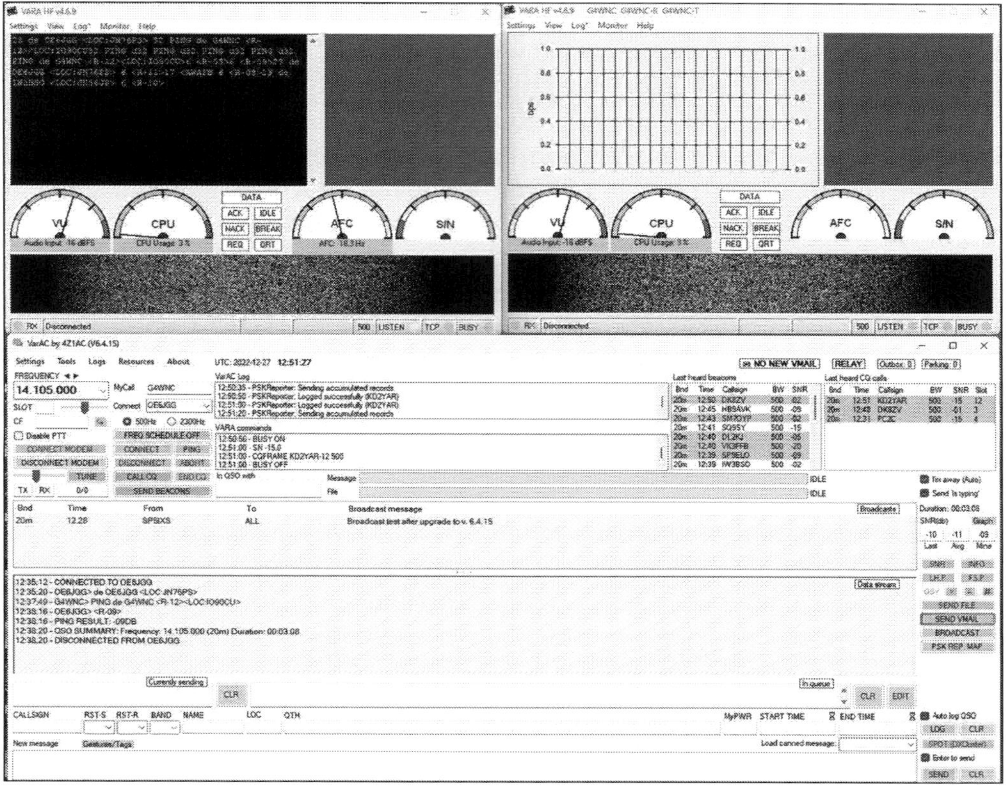

Fig 4.2: VarAC in operation.

Much like its earlier cousin AMTOR, VarAC is a fully error-corrected system, so there is no need for any repeats as the system manages that for you. VarAC also includes measured signal reports and other automation so you can concentrate on chatting. The result is a robust chat system that is rapidly growing in popularity, **Fig 4.2**.

VarAC development has been led by Irad Deutsch, 4Z1AC, and assisted by a team of enthusiasts. The mode name is derived from Irad's callsign and the VARA modem at the heart of the mode. Since its original launch in October 2021, the mode has been under constant development, with new features being added along with user-led improvements and bug fixes. Before we get into the details, let's look at what VarAC offers:

Easy contacts: Calling CQ is an automated process that, in addition to sending your CQ, also manages both parties' QSYing to a working frequency.

Automatic QSO logging: VarAC supports many of the most popular logging programs but also stores your contacts in standard ADIF format, thus making it easy to import to other software.

Rig CAT control: Support for most rigs is included and should be used to get the best from VarAC features.

Spellcheck: VarAC has an integrated spellchecker that works as you type.

Beacons: VarAC includes a beacon mode that operators use to show their availability.

Free format chatting: VarAC makes free text QSOs very straightforward. Once you've connected with a station, signal reports and callsign exchanges happen automatically, so you can start chatting immediately. There's no need to exchange calls between overs and many operators don't use overs in the traditional sense but just chat.

Gestures: You can brighten up your chats by adding sounds and emojis.

'Is Typing': This is a message that appears when the other station is typing and prompts you to pause to see what they have to say.

PSK Reporter link: The PSK Reporter button opens up a PSK Reporter map showing all the stations that have heard your beacon transmissions. This is a valuable propagation check.

Message queue: Typed messages go through three phases. The first is a buffer where you start typing your message. The next phase is a buffer that stores messages before being sent. Finally, the transmit buffer contains messages in the process of being sent. All text in the first two buffers can be edited. It's only when the message drops into the transmit buffer that it's no longer editable.

Canned messages: Similar to macros in other data modes software, canned messages are commonly occurring text that you frequently send, i.e. your rig and antenna details. These can be fully customised and assigned to function keys.

Send files and images: VarAC can send binary files, text and images, though you should restrict this to small files on the HF bands.

Under the Bonnet of VarAC

There are two critical components to VarAC, the first is the VARA modem developed by Jose Ros, EA5HVK, and the second is the VarAC client software by Irad Deutsch, 4Z1AC. Jose pioneered much of the modem development with his ROS-modem system, which became very popular a few years ago. That work evolved into the sophisticated VARA software modem (MODulator DEModulator) that has been very successful.

The VARA modem is available in three forms, VARA-HF, VARA-FM and VARA-SAT. These are intended for use on HF, VHF and the QO-100 satellite respectively. The VARA modem is a variable rate, adaptive modem. By this, I mean that the modems can negotiate and select the optimum link speed for the prevailing band conditions. This negotiation is an ongoing process, and the link speed will automatically adapt as conditions change. The VARA modem also supports packet-like commands, so you can instruct it to connect to another named station. It will then send a connection request and, providing the other station is available, set up an error-corrected link. This link can then send just about any

Level	Symbol Rate	Carriers	Mod type	Rate (bps)
1	23	32	FSK	18
2	47	16	FSK	41
3	47	16	FSK	82
4	94	16	FSK	175
5	94	3	4PSK	270
6	94	4	4PSK	363
7	94	6	4PSK	549
8	94	8	4PSK	735
9	94	10	4PSK	922
10	42	49	4PSK	2011
11	42	49	4PSK	2682
12	42	49	4PSK	3219
13	42	49	8PSK	4025
14	42	49	8PSK	4830
15	42	49	16QAM	5872
16	42	49	32QAM	7050

Table 4.1: VARA-HF modem speeds.

form of data. VARA has become a well-established modem and has been selected for use with the international WinLink HF email system.

In **Table 4.1**, I've shown the data rates and bandwidths available from the VARA modem. VARA uses a variety of modulation systems, but they are all based around the use of Orthogonal Frequency Division Multiplex, OFDM. OFDM utilises several closely-spaced carriers, each modulated with a portion of the data. At the distant end, the multiple carriers are demodulated, and the original data is reassembled, as shown in **Fig 4.3**. The modulation method applied to each OFDM

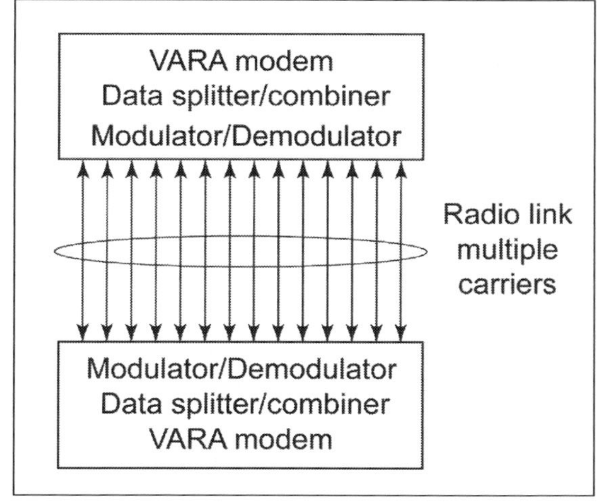

Fig 4.3: OFDM operation.

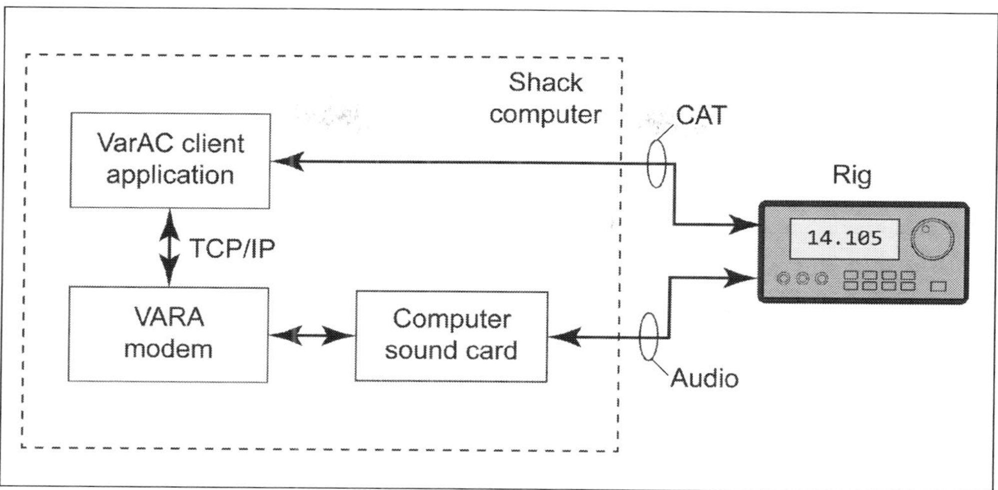

Fig 4.4: VarAC and VARA installation.

subcarrier varies depending on the negotiated link speed. The VARA modem represents a significant investment of time for the author, who has generously allowed the modem to be used free of charge for speeds up to 200 baud. To open up the full range of speeds, a licence fee of 63 euros is required. This licence allows the use of VARA modems on any number of computers, but with a single callsign. The maximum speed available from the licensed modem is 8,499bps when using a 2,750Hz bandwidth. However, these high speeds are unnecessary for keyboard QSOs, and the free tier of up to 200 baud is adequate.

VarAC is an entirely separate application or client that uses the VARA modem to send the data and manage the radio link. VarAC communicates with the VARA modem using commands similar to those used with Packet radio TNCs. All communications between the VARA and the VarAC client are handled via a TCP/IP protocol link. I've shown a diagram of a VarAC installation in **Fig 4.4**. Here you can see the clear separation between the two applications.

What Do You Need?

Like most modern data modes, the VarAC signal is computer-generated and decoded using audio tones that can be applied to, and received from, a standard SSB transceiver. Therefore, your computer will need a sound card with audio inputs and outputs. If you don't have a suitable sound card, one of the readily-available USB sound cards is ideal. You will also need a Windows computer running Windows 8.1 or later. VarAC can also be coaxed to run on a Linux PC, including a Raspberry Pi, by using Box86 and Wine to emulate a Windows environment. More details for running VarAC on Linux are available on the VarAC website at **https://www.varac-hamradio.com**

In addition to the audio ins and outs, VarAC needs some control of your rig. The minimum requirement is control of the PTT line, however, to enjoy all the features of VarAC, full CAT control is essential. Provided you have the dedicated lead to connect your rig to your computer, CAT control should be straightforward. VarAC includes CAT control facilities for most popular rigs. Even if your rig is not included, VarAC can use OmniRig to provide the CAT control facilities.

VARA and VarAC Installation

To use VarAC, you need to install both the VarAC client and the VARA software modem. You should begin by installing the VARA modem, and you can choose VARA-HF, VARA-FM or VARA-SAT. As most of the VarAC activity occurs on the HF bands, I suggest you start with VARA-HF. This is available from the EA5HVK website at **http://rosmodem.wordpress.com**

Here is the step-by-step installation:

1. Download the VARA-HF zip file and unzip the file to a convenient temporary location.
2. Locate the VARA setup file, right-click, choose Properties and, on the General tab, tick Unblock then OK, **Fig 4.5**.
3. Double-click the VARA setup file to start the installation.
4. Follow the prompts and accept the default settings.
5. That completes the VARA-HF installation.

This process will have installed the VARA-HF modem in the VARA folder on your C: drive.

The next step is configuring the VARA-HF modem to use your computer's sound card. Here's a step-by-step guide:

1. Navigate to C:\VARA and double-click on VARA.exe to open the modem, **Fig 4.6**.
2. Use the Settings menu and select SoundCard.
3. Use the drop-down menus to choose your soundcard for the Device input and Device output.
4. You can also use the Tune button in this panel to adjust your transmit audio level.
5. Click Close when finished.

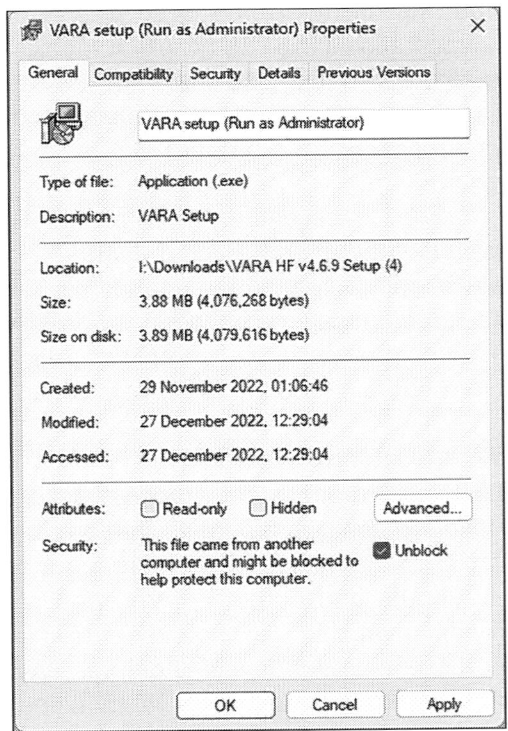

Fig 4.5: Unblocking .exe files.

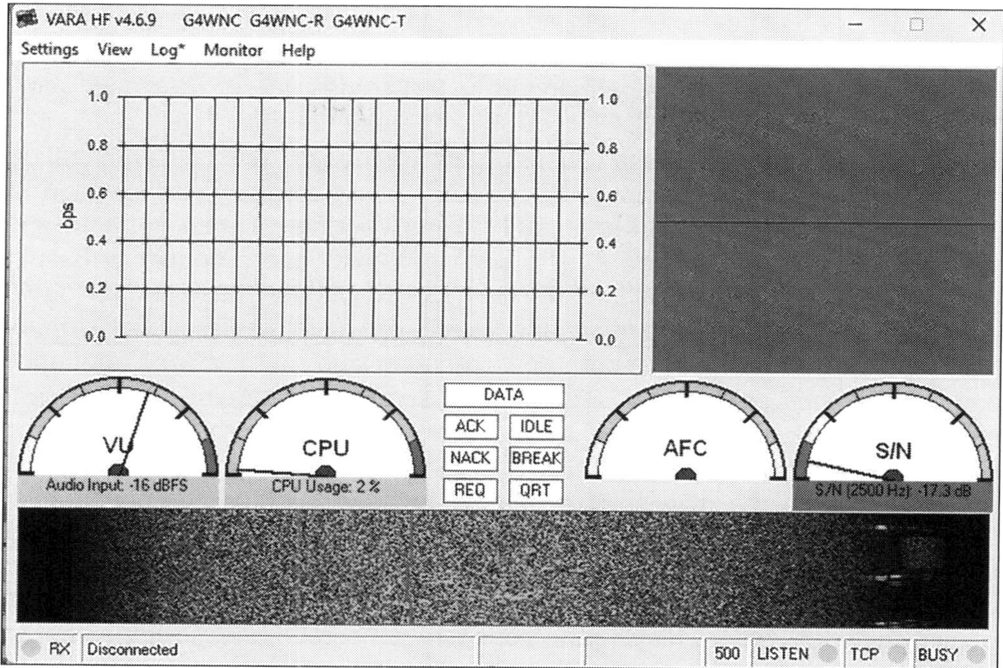

Fig 4.6: The VARA-HF modem.

6. If you've bought the licence for VARA, you can enter your callsign and licence key via the VARA Setup menu.

That completes the configuration of the main modem, but VarAC supports a second instance of the modem to monitor band activity. To enable this, you must copy all the files in the VARA folder and paste them to a new folder on your C: drive. The folder name is unimportant, but I suggest using VARA-Monitor for clarity.

With the VARA-HF modem configured, we can install the VarAC application. This can be downloaded from the VarAC home site at **https://www.varac-hamradio.com**. Before the download begins, you will need to enter your name, callsign and email address. This will download a zip file that you need to expand. Unlike many software packages, VarAC is a stand-alone program, so there is no installer, just unzip the downloaded files to the desired folder on your hard drive. I suggest expanding to a new folder on your C: drive called VarAC. Within the expanded files, locate the VarAC application file, right-click and choose Properties, tick the Unblock box at the bottom of the General tab, and click OK. You can now double-click the VarAC application to begin configuration.

Configuring VarAC

When first starting VarAC, you will be presented with a prompt to enter your callsign and station details. Once complete, you should see the VarAC main screen, where the next step is to continue configuration. Go to the Settings menu and choose Rig control and VARA configuration. Although not essential, full rig control is strongly recommended as it provides a very slick user interface. VarAC has integrated CAT control for the most popular rigs, so you just need to select your rig from the two drop-down menus in the PTT Configuration and Frequency Control sections. Under CAT Configuration you also need to enter details of the COM port and baud rate for your rig.

Once you have completed the rig control, VarAC has a couple of built-in tests you can use. The first is the PTT On and Off buttons. These should toggle your PTT on / off. Next is the mode and frequency test in the Frequency Control section. Here you can use the drop-down menu to select a mode and frequency combination then press the TEST button to send the commands to the rig. If these tests work, you can relax, as you have full CAT control. I've shown an example configuration in **Fig 4.7**.

The last part of the initial setup is to move to the VARA Modem Configuration section. Here the modem type should be VaraHF and the VARA file path should point to your installation, which is normally C:\VARA\VARA.exe. However, you will need to set the VARA monitor path to C:\Vara-Monitor if you followed my earlier guidance. Before leaving the configuration screen, please remember to click the Save and Exit button at the bottom.

Close and restart VarAC and you are ready to start monitoring.

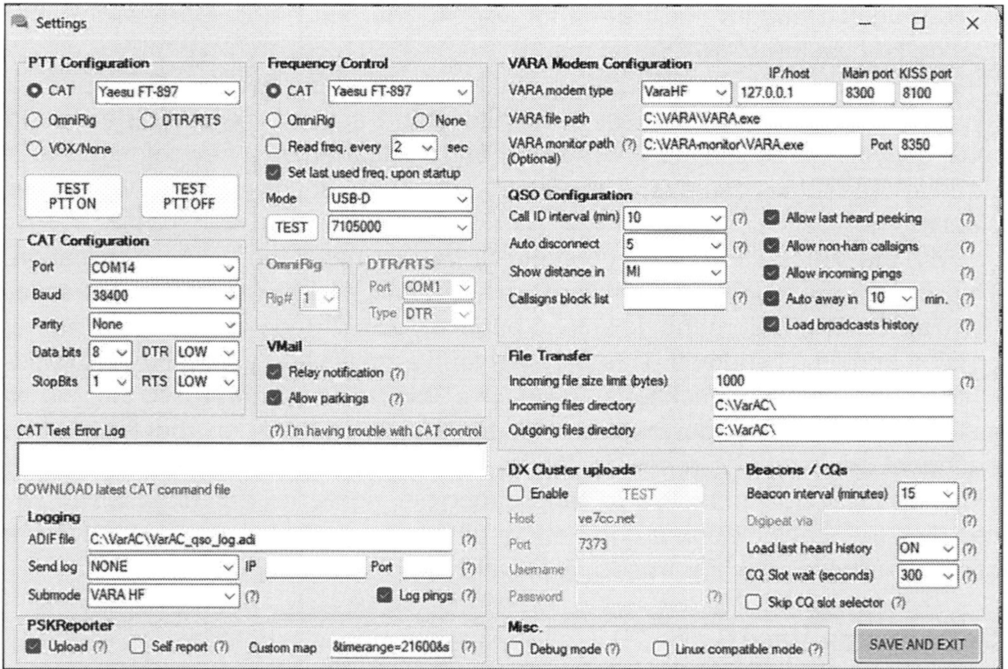

Fig 4.7: VarAC CAT configuration example.

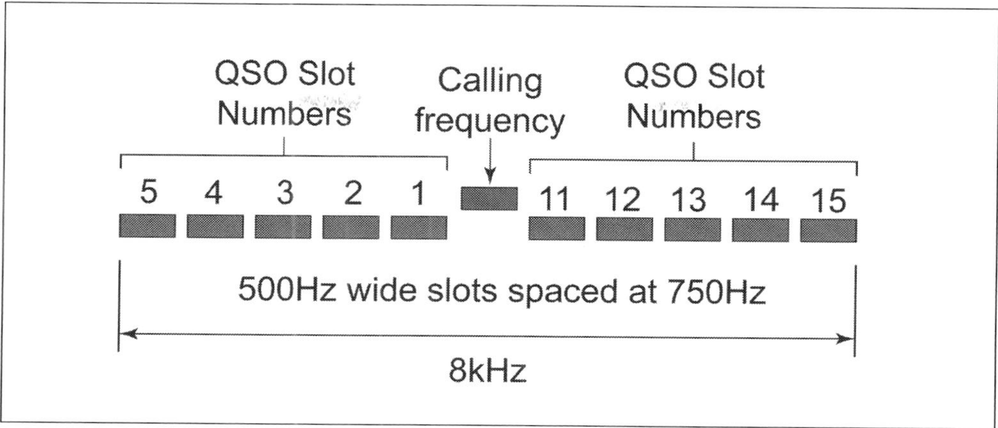

Fig 4.8: VarAC slot system.

Operating VarAC

Because each VarAC transmission occupies a 500Hz bandwidth, it is not possible to run all the band activity in a single voice channel, as is the case with FT8, FT4, PSK31 and other very narrow-band modes. The wider bandwidth of VarAC demands a new band plan. The system currently adopted is to set a calling frequency on each band (see **Table 3.1** on page 30) and allocate five 750Hz-spaced slots above and below the calling frequency, as shown in **Fig 4.8**.

A calling channel is particularly helpful for a new mode like VarAC because it concentrates the activity on that frequency. As a further aid, VarAC supports the use of beacon transmissions. These are short transmissions on the calling frequency that provide basic callsign information. It's primarily a way of advertising that your station is 'online'. However, please don't send beacons if your station is unattended or if you cannot respond to a contact request. Unattended beacons just lead to disappointment for those trying to initiate QSOs.

The default beacon transmission frequency is 15 minutes, and you can activate the beacon using the SEND BEACONS button on the VarAC main screen.

RF Power Levels

The VARA modem that manages the radio link uses very efficient coding and modulation so high powers are rarely necessary. Most operators have settled on between 10 and 20 watts as a good power level for everyday communications. You should also take note of your reported signal level and reduce power if you have an SNR report better than 0dB.

Upgrading

The rapid ongoing development of VarAC means you will need to periodically update the software. Some of the VarAC enhancements also require an update to the VARA modem, so a dual upgrade is occasionally necessary. However, the upgrade process is simple and I've shown step-by-step guides here:

First, upgrading VarAC:

1. Download the latest VarAC version from the VarAC website: **https://www.varac-hamradio.com/download**
2. Expand the zip file to a convenient temporary folder.
3. Copy the VarAC.exe application and the VarAC_cat_commands.ini files to your VarAC installation folder. Normally C:\VarAC
4. In the VarAC application folder, right-click on the VarAC application and choose Properties and tick Unblock on the General tab.

That's it!

Next, upgrading VARA-HF modem:

1. Download the latest VARA-HF modem from: **https://rosmodem.wordpress.com**
2. Expand the zip file to a convenient temporary location.
3. Right-click on the installation file (VARA setup (Run as administrator). On the general tab click Unblock.
4. Double-click on the VARA setup (Run as administrator) file to start the installation.
5. Follow the prompts and accept the default directory.

If you are using a second instance of VARA-HF for monitoring, you will also need to copy all the files in the C:\VARA folder to the location of the second instance (normally C:\Vara-monitor).

This is the recommended upgrade process at the time of writing, but this may change as the software develops, so please refer to the VarAC website (**varac-hamradio.com**) for the latest information.

Making a Contact

The VarAC authors have made the contact process as simple as possible, though it may seem alien at first. There are essentially four ways to make a contact, as follows:

1. Respond to a CQ call;
2. Connect to a beacon station;
3. Make a CQ call;
4. Connect to a named station.

Let's run through these in turn:

1: Responding to a CQ is very easy as all CQ calls are listed in the Last heard CQ panel at the top right of the main screen. To respond to a CQ call, you simply double-click on the call in the CQ panel. However, there is one important point to note. CQ calls include automated QSY information and operators normally only wait five minutes after the initial call before they abandon. Because of this, it's important to check the timestamp of the CQ call in the Last heard CQ panel before you respond.

2: Connecting to a beacon station is the simplest option as you just right-click on the beacon station in the last heard beacons panel and select Connect. An important point to note here is that you will be connecting on the calling frequency. Whilst it's OK to make a short QSO on the calling frequency, if the QSO lasts more than a few minutes, you should use the QSY process (see later section) to change frequency.

3: Making a CQ call is an automated process but you have to decide on your QSY frequency before you make the call. This is necessary because VarAC, rather cleverly, includes the QSY information with the CQ call. When you click the CQ button the CQ Slot Selector panel will pop-up, **Fig 4.9**. This is fully explained on screen and takes you through a three-step process. The first step is to choose a slot for the QSO. Next you click and hold the Slot Sniffer button. This temporarily retunes your rig to the slot frequency so you can make sure it's free. If all is well, you move to the final stage and click Call CQ. This will cause the rig to put out a CQ call on the main calling frequency and then wait on the

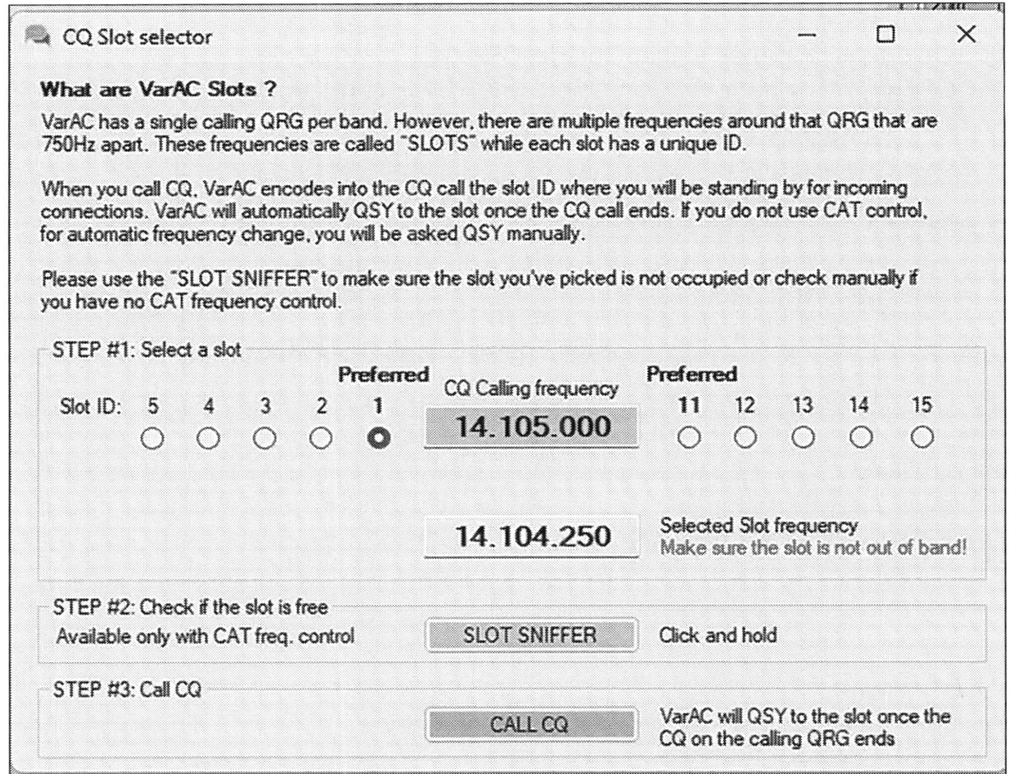

Fig 4.9: VarAC CQ slot selector panel.

chosen QSY slot for a call. After five minutes VarAC will abandon the CQ and retune to the calling frequency.

4: Connecting to a named station is the least used option and for this you enter a target callsign in the connect window (just below your callsign) and press the Connect button. VarAC will then start a connection attempt with the target station. If you make the connection on the calling frequency, don't forget to use the QSY process to continue your QSO.

Automated QSY Process

When a contact has been initiated on the calling frequency, you will need to QSY if the call is likely to last more than a few minutes. To simplify QSYing, VarAC includes a helpful QSY tool. This is found in the right-hand panel, **Fig 4.10**, but is only available when you have an active connection. In the QSY panel, you can use the up and down arrows to shift frequency in 750Hz steps but the '#' button is more useful. This button opens a panel similar to the CQ panel, **Fig 4.11**, where you can select and

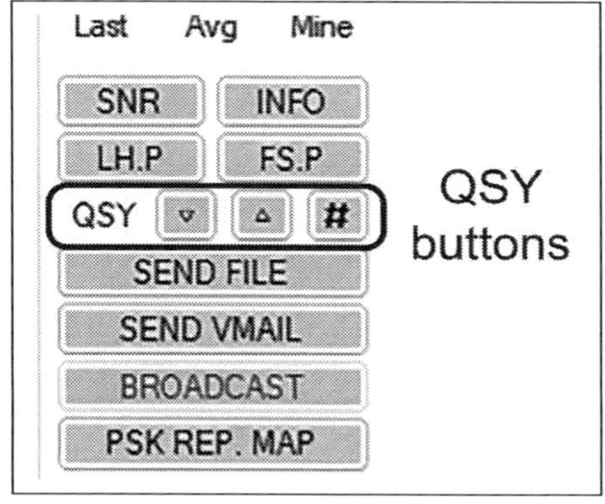

Fig 4.10: VarAC QSY buttons.

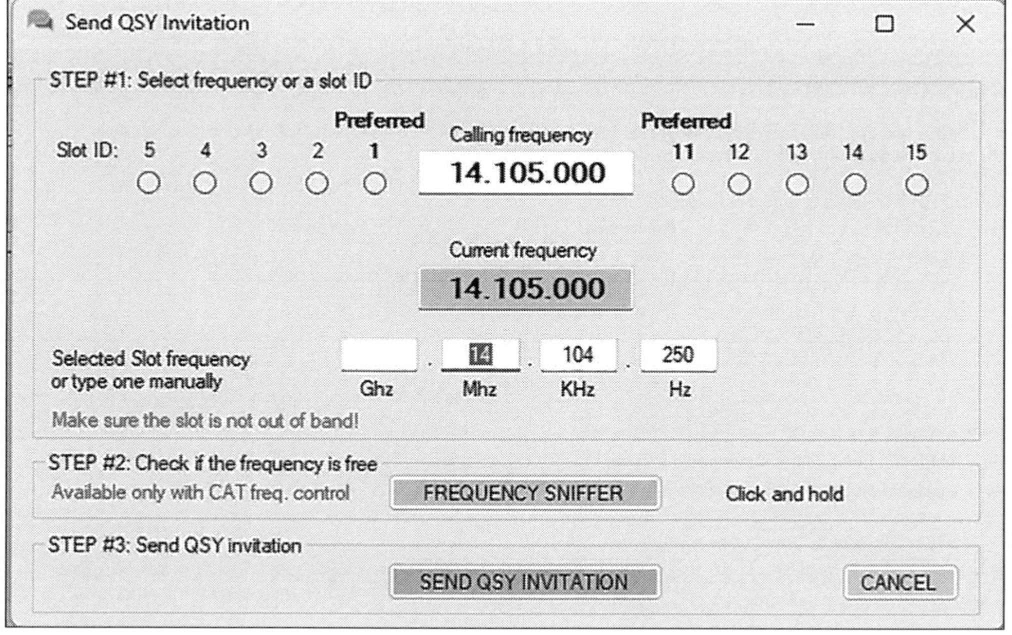

Fig 4.11: VarAC QSY slot selection.

sage. To avoid the calling frequency getting clogged with long messages, the Vmail system is limited to 50 characters in the title field and 300 characters in the message body. Once you've composed your Vmail, it will sit in your outbox until you connect with the target station. However, if you receive a beacon from the target station, VarAC will automatically connect to advise the remote station that a Vmail awaits them.

An alternative delivery arrangement is to use an intermediate station. For example, if you want to send a message to a UK amateur but don't have a good path, you could select an European station that you can both reach and leave the Vmail on their computer. Next time your colleague connects with that station, the Vmail will be delivered. To deposit the Vmail with the intermediate station, you have to first connect with that station and then right-click and choose Send Vmail now.

VarAC Summary

The introduction of VarAC has brought a fresh look to data modes on the HF bands and encouraged more amateurs to engage in conversations. The software is also enjoying ongoing development and becoming an ever more sophisticated system. If you enjoy the mode, I encourage you to join the Forum and Facebook group to share your enthusiasm with the team.

THE FUTURE OF DIGITAL MODES

Keyboard modes such as JS8 and VarAC may well be the future of HF digital modes, but it is also clear that FT8 and, later, FT4 filled a gap that attracted many amateurs to digimode operating, often for the first time. The fixed-format modes are likely to undergo further development along the lines of Fox and Hounds in WSJT-X or DXpedition multi-streaming in MSHV in order to improve their performance for DXers and contesters, while JS8 and VarAC will also continue to be enhanced for those who prefer to chat using digital modes.

There is no doubt that the WSJT suite of programs, and in particular FT8, brought datamodes into the 21st century and that they have now entered the amateur radio mainstream. It is clear that both fixed-format and keyboard modes will continue to play a significant role in amateur radio's future.

RSGB BOOKSHOP

Always the best Amateur Radio books

Work The World With DMR

Digital Mobile Radio Explained

By Andrew Barron, ZL3DW

As many will have already discovered, getting started in Digital Mobile Radio (DMR) can be tricky. This book from well-known author Andrew Barron, ZL3DW provides his usual practical approach to the subject. He provides the information you need to get started with this exciting digital voice technology. Before you know it, you will be able to talk with amateur radio operators all over the world.

The *Work the World with DMR* practical approach explains the steps that you need to follow to make your new DMR radio work on your local repeater or hotspot, and for worldwide contacts. Amateur Radio DMR is not as simple as entering a couple of frequencies and setting a CTCSS tone the way you would for an FM radio. So, you can expect a steep learning curve but of course that's where this book will be the most helpful. You will discover lots of new terms including dashboards, zones, receive groups, colour codes, code plugs, hotspots, Parrot, talk groups, and time slots. Also, acronyms like MMDVM, CPS, IPSC2, DMR-MARC, TGIF, and DMR+. MMDVM (multi-mode digital voice modem) 'hotspots' are very popular accessories and there is information here about their uses and configuration. You will also find coverage of duplex hotspots and the perhaps more familiar simplex hotspots, including a section on how to assemble a hotspot from a kit, a Raspberry Pi, and an SD card. There is even step by step instructions for configuring the Pi-Star hotspot operating system.

For anyone interested in DMR or simply looking to expand their knowledge, *Work the World with DMR* will help you to become familiar with the complex terminology used by the DMR crowd, purchase and program a DMR radio, and make your first few calls, configure and use a DMR hotspot, use DMR repeaters, talk groups and much more besides.

Size 176x240mm, 224 Pages

ISBN: 9781913995188

ONLY £16.99

www.rsgbshop.org FROM FREE P&P on orders over £30. See T&Cs

Radio Society of Great Britain, 3 Abbey Court, Priory Business Park, Bedford, MK44 3WH Tel: 01234 8327

5. Technical Background to the Digital Modes

The aim of this chapter is to cover the technical background to digital modes, to explain how they work and to give some reasons for their high performance in the weak-signal regime of the DX QSO. We start with a primer on the relevant digital electronics, since this is barely covered in the average amateur enthusiast's training. This leads to an overview of a generic digital transmission system where the component parts are briefly explained. We then go into further detail of each one of these components. The mathematical background is kept to an absolute minimum and, where possible, diagrams are used in place of mathematical rigour. Examples from amateur digital modes are used where possible to link the theory to the practical amateur communications world.

DIGITAL TECHNOLOGY IN THE ANALOGUE WORLD

Obviously, digital modes rely on digital techniques and that means we are in the realm of bits, bytes and codes. Linking these together is mathematics and software. It is well known that these are complex topics, and maybe beyond the average amateur to experiment with, but this is only partly true. They are complex but not beyond us amateurs. I will try to explain the magic behind these digital modes without the use of advanced mathematics.

The basis of digital systems is binary representation: everything is measured in bits. A bit is either '1' or '0' and groups of eight bits are termed a byte. Long before digital systems entered everyday life, mathematics had studied the properties of bits and bytes in binary arithmetic. Of course, this is also the basis of computers and their software. Digital modes can be described as a fusion of communications and computers. Both of these areas also need to relate to us and we, of course, do not 'speak' binary so we need to link the digital domain to the real world of electronics, analogue voltages, and human language. This is achieved using analogue to digital converters and codes.

The English alphabet has been coded into binary many times using several codes, but the most significant one is the American Standard Code for Information Interchange, or *ASCII* for short. This code gives each character a seven-bit code. For example, lower case 'a' is 1100001, whilst capital 'A' is 1000001 and the number '1' is 0110001. These binary numbers could be written as their decimal equivalents: 'a' = 97, 'A' = 65 and '1' is 49 but this is not normal practice. A more common technique is to use the hexadecimal numbering system. As the name suggests, this uses a base of sixteen, whereas our familiar decimal system uses a base of ten. For example, the ASCII letter 'a' is 97 when written in decimal, because it is comprised of nine 10s and seven 1s or units. In the hexadecimal numbering scheme, the same number would be written as 61. This is because it is made up of six 16s and one 1 or unit. I'm sure you can see that there is potential for great confusion should decimal and hexadecimal numbers get intermixed. To avoid this, it is common practice to prefix a hexadecimal number when used in mixed numbering situations. The standard prefix is 0x so the letter 'a' in our example would be written as 0x61 in hexadecimal. One other point to note about hexadecimal is the characters we use. In decimal we use the digits 0

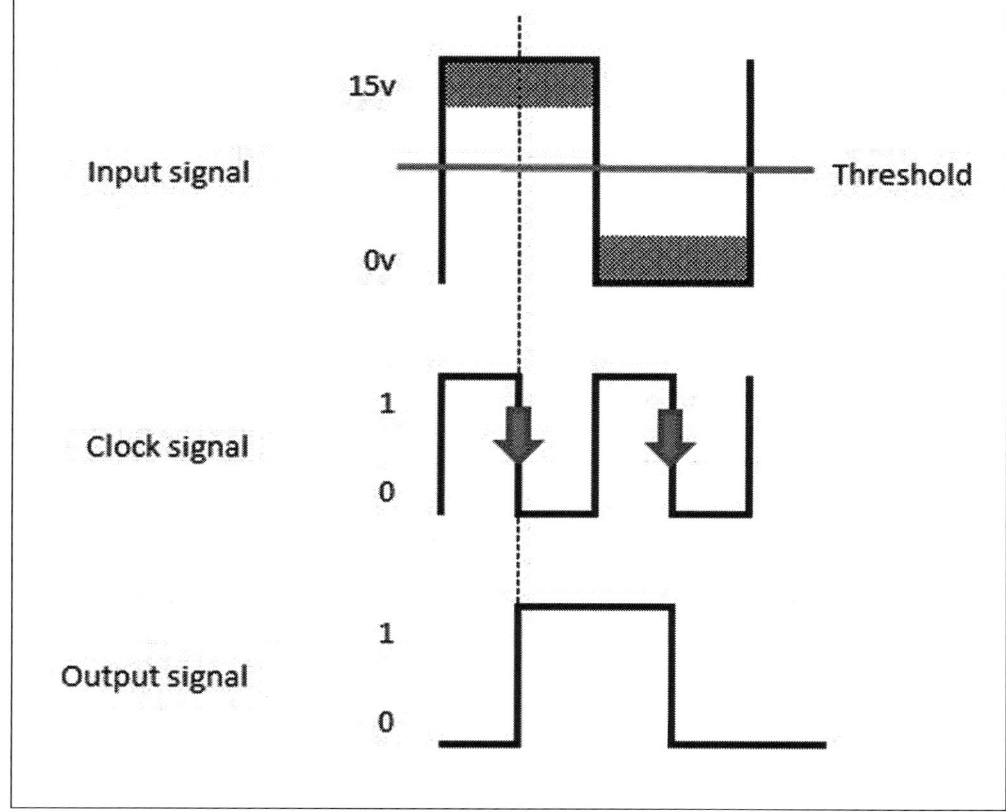

Fig 5.1: The clock signal controls the timing of a digital system.

through to 9 but we need more to cope with hexadecimal. The solution is to extend the numbers with alphabetic characters. As a result, hexadecimal uses the following mix of numerical and alphabetic characters: 0, 1, 2, 3, 4, 5, 6, 7, 8, 9, a, b, c, d, e, f. Using this scheme, the decimal number 15 would be written as 0x0f in hexadecimal.

Whilst binary data is just a series of 0s and 1s, in computing the data is represented by differing voltage levels. Many different voltage standards exist, for example, TTL logic levels are based on a 5V supply, whereas many of today's systems use much lower voltages. The lower voltage systems save power but are more susceptible to noise. In practical systems, it is not possible to have the voltage swing from exactly 0 to 5V to indicate logic 0 or 1, so a threshold is used. In a TTL system, a voltage higher than 2V is treated as a logic 1, whilst a signal lower than 0.8V is a logic 0. Similar thresholds are used for other logic systems to enable analogue voltage changes to be converted into a digital data stream.

There is one other dimension before we can form a data stream, and that is time. When do we make the threshold decisions? To do this, we introduce the concept of a digital clock. This is merely a square wave of constant period or frequency that determines the time at which we apply the thresholds to the voltage waveform. Now we can see how the input signal at the top in **Fig 5.1** is turned into the binary data stream below. This is termed a synchronous data stream because it uses a clock to synchronise the data.

In terms of serial data communications, we still have one more thing to achieve. If this data stream was a series of letters making up a message, we still need to know when each letter code starts and finishes. One way to do this is to make the start and finish of each letter code unique in some way. A simple way to do this is to add a start and stop bit as shown in **Fig 5.2**. The start bit is a transition from high to low that tells the receiver to expect a data package, in this case a four-bit sequence 1110 followed by a stop bit which is a transition from low to high. The key is that the timing between start and stop bits is known by the

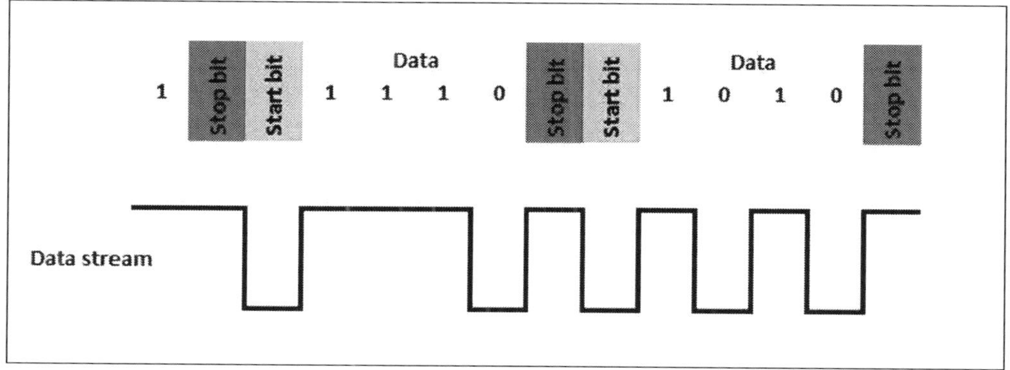

Fig 5.2: Start and Stop bits define the data.

receiving system so it can synchronise the data by looking for this pattern. As we will see later, adding more bits to the basic message is a common activity in serial data communications.

HOW DIGITAL TECHNOLOGY INTERFACES TO THE ANALOGUE WORLD

The other aspect is linking the real world of analogue to the digital domain. An *analogue to digital converter* (ADC) and its inverse, a *digital to analogue converter* (DAC), are the items that do this task. First of all, let's consider a simple signal that should be familiar to all radio amateurs: the sine wave, representing an AC voltage.

This could represent anything from AC mains through to an RF microwave signal. The key characteristics are amplitude and frequency (or period). That shown in **Fig 5.3** is a 100Hz 2V peak-to-peak waveform. To convert this into the digital domain, we measure the waveform at regular intervals of time – every T_s seconds. We term $1/T_s$ the sampling frequency or rate and each measurement is termed a *sample*. **Fig 5.4** shows an expanded version of the first part of **Fig 5.3** with the sampling points marked. The table on the right-hand side of **Fig 5.4** shows the samples taken every 500µs, which is a 2kHz sampling rate. The second column shows the voltage of the waveform at the time the sample was taken. The ADC converts this voltage to a binary number but, for convenience the third column is in decimal not binary.

In this example, the output values range between 512 and 1024, but the full range is 0 to 1024, with the values between 0 and 512 being used for the values –1 to 0 volts. The example in **Fig 5.4**, is a 10-bit ADC, which means it outputs

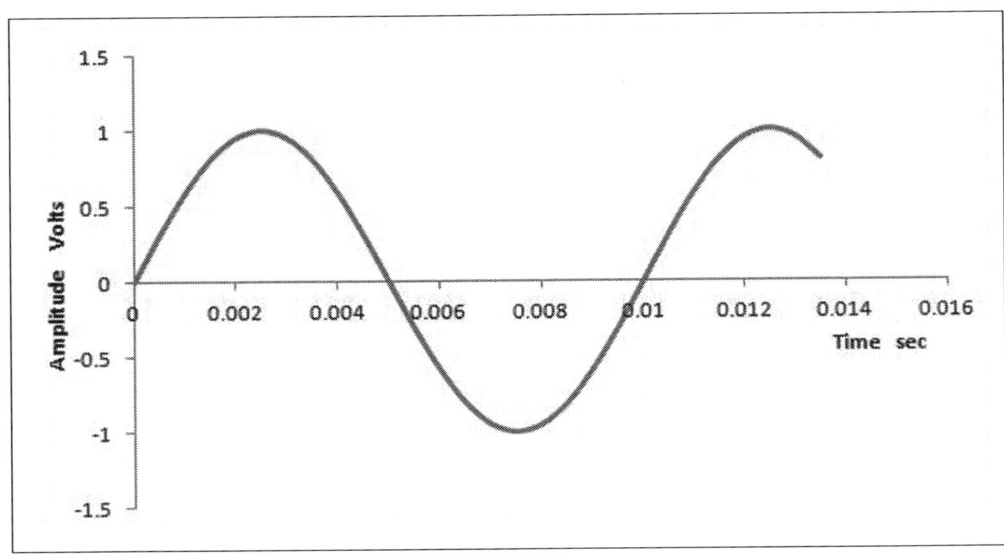

Fig 5.3: Amplitude versus time waveform.

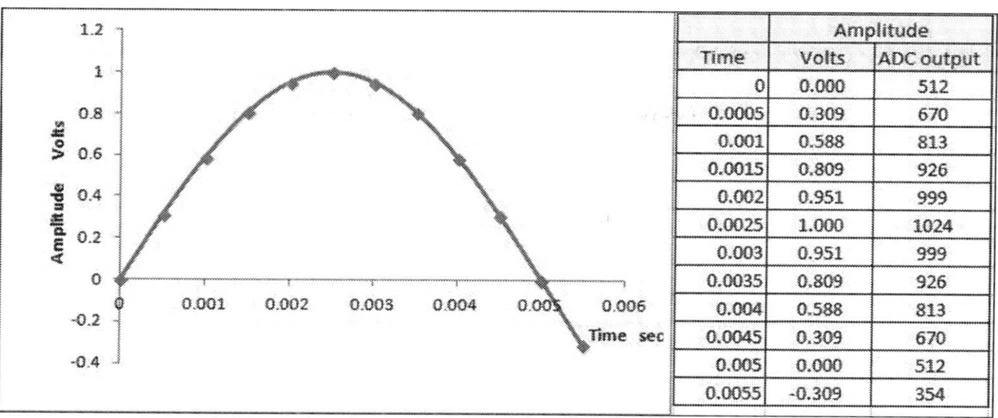

Time	Amplitude	
	Volts	ADC output
0	0.000	512
0.0005	0.309	670
0.001	0.588	813
0.0015	0.809	926
0.002	0.951	999
0.0025	1.000	1024
0.003	0.951	999
0.0035	0.809	926
0.004	0.588	813
0.0045	0.309	670
0.005	0.000	512
0.0055	-0.309	354

Fig 5.4: ADC converts a waveform to digits.

binary values between 0 and 210 (1024 in decimal notation). So, the sample at time 0.001 sec is 1100101101 (813 in decimal notation). These samples form a binary data stream that the ADC software will write directly into memory. Software that is used to directly control hardware, such as the ADC, is known as firmware and usually resides in non-volatile memory as part of the ADC chip.

It is becoming increasingly common to integrate much of the core functionality (ADC, controller and memory) into a single chip that can be used as a building block for more complex systems. The typical modern PC sound card uses an audio codec that meets Intel's High Definition Audio standard. This includes a 16-bit ADC which can output 16-bit binary samples at a sampling rate of 48kHz. Software applications such as WSJT-X will store these values in memory ready for further processing.

The digital to analogue converter is the inverse of the ADC. It takes a binary value and produces the corresponding analogue voltage so that, given a stream of binary values, it can produce a waveform of voltage versus time. The frequency of this waveform depends upon the rate at which the samples are converted back to analogue voltages. This is often linked to an external digital clock that is the equivalent of the sampling rate of the ADC. By varying the clock frequency, you can alter the frequency of the output waveform.

In **Fig 5.4** the Time column in the table shows a steadily increasing time which in the case of the ADC was the sampling points. If, instead of sampling, we generate a clock with the same period and use this to clock a DAC whilst reading the binary values given in the 'ADC output' column, now held in memory, into the DAC, we can generate the sine wave directly. It will appear at the DAC's output as a changing analogue voltage. This is the principle of direct frequency synthesis. In practice filters are required to clean up the output.

The PC sound card codec will also perform the DAC function at sample rates of up to 192kHz and sample depths of 8 to 32 bits. This is more than adequate for the generation of the tones used in HF digital modes.

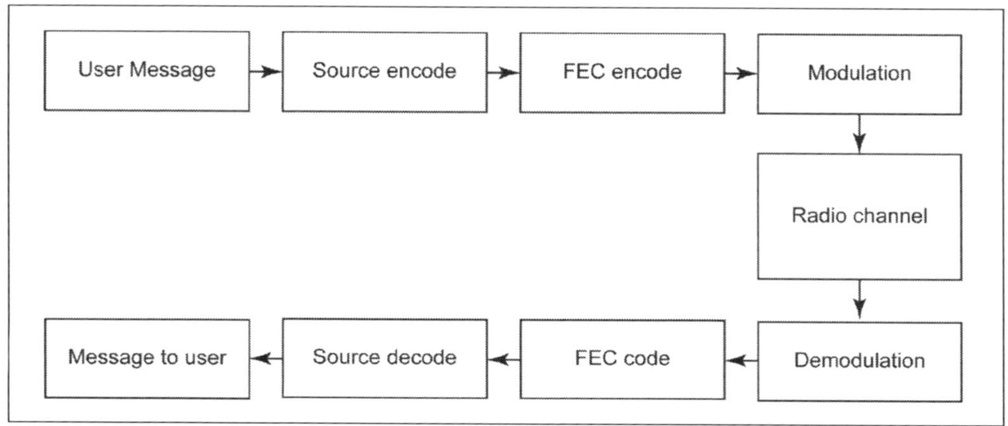

Fig 5.5: Information flow in a digital communication system.

OVERVIEW OF A DIGITAL TRANSMISSION SYSTEM

A modern digital transmission system is shown in **Fig 5.5**. It shows the information flow through the individual stages that make up the system. It begins at the top left with the user message that, in our terms, will consist of amateur callsigns, signal reports, location information, salutations and perhaps other station information or matters of a personal nature.

However, there are two distinct categories of messages: structured messages that just contain the absolute minimum of information to establish a QSO and the more open-ended and freely structured message. The WSJT suite of digital modes caters for the former category of message, whilst the open-ended, sometimes called *keyboard mode*, messages are sent using RTTY and PSK31 modes.

Both message types benefit from some form of message compression to reduce the length of the message to be sent over the air and this is achieved using some form of encoding. WSJT modes use a very structured message that can compress the message into fewer than 75-bits. PSK31 uses a specific alphabet coding called varicode that also reduces the message length.

Having made the effort to reduce the number of information bits in the message, we now expand the message by introducing error control coding: *forward error correction* (FEC). This is a major topic in digital communications and information science and is responsible for the accurate transmission of digital data from storage devices, such as hard drives and DVDs, as well as satellites which provide us with HD TV. It is also vitally important in the communications over immense distances between the Earth and the many interplanetary probes. FEC is used in all of the WSJT modes as well as QPSK31, a variant of PSK31.

Digital communication uses a different modulation of the RF carrier from speech (analogue) signals. However, the two types of modulation are closely related and common digital modulation techniques, such as frequency shift keying (FSK), are easily achievable using amateur equipment.

The radio channel itself is, of course, the same for both analogue and digital transmission. Some of the annoying characteristics such as fading, noise, multipath distortion and Doppler shift become more important for the successful and accurate transmission of digital data. It is often these characteristics that determine the design of the other parts of the system: modulation technique and FEC for example.

Finally, at the receiving end of the communication system, we must demodulate and decode the signal to restore the original message. Sometimes this is a straightforward inverse of the encoding techniques, but often it involves different and quite complex methods. For example, in the case of FEC, the encoding and decoding often use different techniques.

SOURCE ENCODING

The purpose of source encoding is to remove redundant information from the message before it is sent, thus making the process more efficient. If you have ever used file compression on your computer then you have used a form of source encoding. In amateur digital communications, two methods are common: one for structured messages like those in the WSJT modes and one for keyboard modes such as PSK31.

In the WSJT modes, the nature of the message to be sent is used to reduce the message size. Basic amateur QSOs follow a set pattern: exchange of callsigns, location, signal reports and some form of confirmation. Since the world's callsigns confirm to a set pattern, and we already have a way of giving signal reports, this leads to a straightforward compression method.

Callsigns (generally) consist of a one or two character prefix, which includes at least one letter, followed by a number and a suffix of one to three letters. Given the 26 letter alphabet and 10 digits we have a total of 36 possible characters. If we add the null character, then this makes 27 and 37 respectively. The number of all possible callsigns is then 37 x 36 x 10 x 27 x 27 x 27 which is over 262 million, which is less than 2^{28}. Thus, we can code any callsign into 28 bits and, in fact, more than six million of the possible callsigns are not needed and can be used for other messages such as CQ.

The standard method of giving location is by using the Maidenhead grid locator, and there are 180 x 180 of these world-wide, giving a total of 32,400, which is less than 2^{15} so we only need 15 bits to code the location. Thus, the standard QSO exchange of two callsigns, location or signal report or acknowledgement can be encoded into 28 + 28 + 15 = 71 bits. If we add four more bits to indicate alternative message structures then we have a total of 75 bits. This can be compared to the use of ASCII text that would use 100 – 136 bits, nearly twice as many. As we will see later, this would be expanded again when error control is added, so any efficiency gains at this early stage affect the final message size dramatically.

FT8 employed the 75-bit message format in all versions up to version 1.9 but in version 2.0 this changed to a 77-bit message. This enabled some new features such as:

- Improved North American VHF contesting operation with full support to /R callsigns;
- European VHF Contesting operation with six digit locator grids, QSO serial numbers and /P callsigns;
- ARRL Field Day operation with standard Field Day exchanges;
- Improved support for non-standard callsigns;
- A new message format to allow for the exchange of 71-bits of arbitrary information.

Changing the message source encoding is not backwards compatible so users of the older versions had to upgrade. Since this is free software it should not impose a burden on the user.

Such compression techniques cannot be directly applied to the keyboard modes such as PSK31 because, by their very nature, messages sent directly from a keyboard are less structured. However, we can make use of the frequency that each letter is used in a typical message to design the alphabetic code. Instead of using 7 bits for every character, as in the ASCII code, we could adjust the number of bits for each letter. In English, the most common letter is 'e' and the least common 'z'. So, if we use '11' as the code for 'e' but '111010101' for 'z' we will be optimising the code for English. This is the basis of varicode alphabets.

A recent development created JS8Call, a hybrid keyboard mode, which breaks free text messages down into blocks that can be sent using FT8 source encoding, as described in Chapter 4.

ERROR DETECTION

The human ear and brain are very good at deciphering information that is mixed with noise and even other sounds and conversations. It is this skill that both CW and SSB operators put to great effect when they drag weak DX stations out from the chaos of an HF pile-up. A few mistakes can be tolerated and often common sense can fill in the missing information caused by erroneous reception. However, digital messages are far less forgiving of errors, and techniques to improve the accurate communication of digital data now form a major branch of communications theory. It is nice to know that radio amateurs are making full use of this theory and no doubt will continue to contribute to its development in the future.

When conversing with someone, errors or miscommunications are easily handled simply by asking the person to repeat the part we missed. However, life is more complex with digital messages because we first need to be able to detect that an error has occurred. One simple way is to use what's known as a *parity check* and there are two variations, odd or even parity. To use even parity checking, each character of the message being sent is examined to count the total number of logic 1s, and an extra bit is then added and set to either 1 or 0 to make an even number of logic 1s. At the receiving end, each character is examined again, and those with an even number of 1s are accepted, whilst the rest are assumed to be damaged and are rejected. Odd parity uses the same technique, except the extra bit is used to create an odd number of 1s. Parity checking is simple to implement with a low overhead but can easily be fooled if several bits have been corrupted.

An extension of the parity error detection method is the *cyclic redundancy check* (CRC). This is slightly more complex but offers the ability to detect multiple errors at the expense of adding more bits to the original message. It is normally used on larger blocks of data than the parity technique. One of the key requirements of any error checking method is that it must be capable of being implemented using logic blocks that are commonly available in electronic circuits. The CRC calculation is based upon the exclusive OR function, which returns a 1 only if the inputs are different and is set out similar to long division. It is easier to understand if you follow the example in **Fig 5.6**.

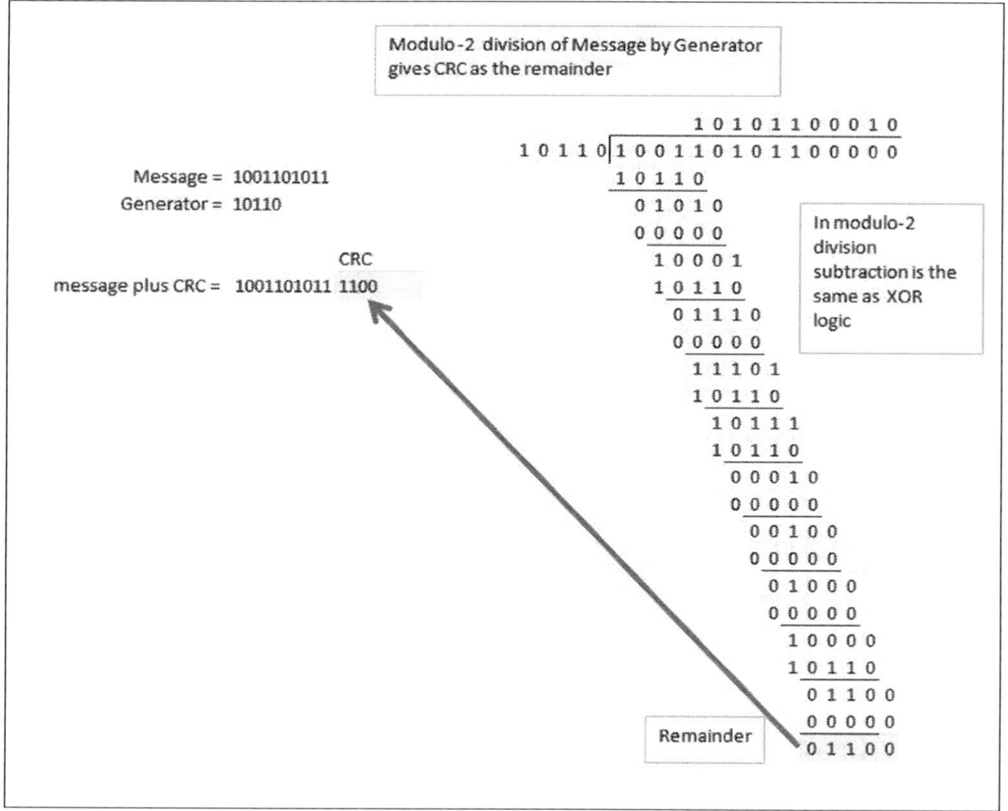

Fig 5.6: Example CRC calculation.

The message is padded out with zeros according to the length of the generator that, in this case, is 10110. This generator is known to both the sender and the recipient of the message and is often described in the protocol, if this is a commercial system, for example CCIT X-25 uses 1000100000010001.

The padded-out message is then divided by the generator using a particular form of division termed modulo-2 that is easily implemented using XOR logic gates. The remainder from this process is appended to the message as the CRC. It is then easy for the received message to be checked – the receiver just carries out the same calculation on the message part of the received data and compares its calculated CRC to the received CRC. If they are the same, the message is deemed error free. If not, errors have been detected, though not identified.

Parity and CRC are similar methods and they only allow you to detect errors and hence confirm the message integrity. They are often combined with a method to request the sender to repeat the erroneous message in a hope that it will be received correctly the next time. These methods are termed *automatic request* (ARQ) methods. ARQ is used in the amateur teletype over radio (AMTOR) mode..

FORWARD ERROR CORRECTION

Whilst it is useful to know if the message has errors, it would be better if we could also correct the errors in the received data. This is the aim of *forward error correction* (FEC). This has been the focus of much research as digital communications have become ever more important. FEC is used in controlling the errors in the transmission of data from DVDs, hard drives, tapes as well as satellite TV and DAB radio. It is a large and, at times, complex topic that is based upon relatively obscure mathematics; however, it is possible to grasp the basics without recourse to too much maths.

The basic FEC concept is counter-intuitive. To reduce the likelihood of errors in a message, we increase the message length, turning say a 12-bit message into 120-bits! How can this possibly work? Surely, the likelihood of an error *increases* with the length of the message? This becomes even more surprising if we keep the transmit time of the message the same as for the original mes-

Hamming distance						
	ASCI code		1100001	1100010	1100011	1100100
Letter	Decimal	binary				
a	97	1100001	0	2	1	1
b	98	1100010	2	0	1	2
c	99	1100011	1	1	0	3
d	100	1100100	2	1	3	0

Table 5.1: Hamming distance between ASCI characters.

sage. With the transmitted energy the same for both, the critical measure of energy per bit is reduced, thus making the signal-to-noise ratio worse. However, this technique does really work, and it is the basis of all FEC.

Consider a simple example: we wish to send a simple message consisting of ASCII characters and we know from our previous discussion that these characters are represented as 7-bit binary numbers. The first four letters are shown in **Table 5.1** where we can see that the letter 'b' is represented by 1100010_b in binary whilst the letter 'a' is 1100001_b. We can see that the difference between these two representations is the last two digits: 'a' ends in 01_b whilst 'b' ends in 10_b. This difference can be measured not only as an increase of 1, 01_b= 1 whilst 10_b= 2, but also as the number of changes that are required to change 01_b to 10_b which is two changes. This number of changes to convert one binary number to another is called the *Hamming distance* and it is a useful measure when we are considering errors – because errors are just that, changes from the original code. **Table 5.1** also shows the Hamming distance between the first four letters.

As you can see, the Hamming distance is small. In fact, just changing a single bit to the opposite will change the letter code to another character. This is made clear in **Table 5.2** which shows the effect of a single error on each of the bits in the character 'b'. This single error can change the received character from 'b' to 'r', 'j', 'f' etc.

If we now change the representation of the characters from a 7-bit representation to a larger one, say 20 bits, we can do the same analysis again. The 20-bit codewords that represent the ASCII characters are, for this example, chosen at random. **Table 5.3** shows the Hamming distance between these random codewords and, as you can see, it is much larger than the original 7-bit codes. So how does this help? Well, let us imagine that we receive a 20-bit codeword that has several errors.

Actual value	
1100010	b
Single bit error	
100010	"
1000010	B
1110010	r
1101010	j
1100110	f
1100000	'
1100011	c

Table 5.2: Single bit errors.

Hamming distance					
20bit codeword	Letter	a	b	c	d
11011001001001100101	a	0	8	9	13
10011000010000101011	b	8	0	9	9
11110100011000011101	c	9	9	0	8
10110010110010111100	d	13	9	8	0

Table 5.3: Codeword with three errors Hamming distance.

Hamming distance		
20bit codeword	Letter	10001001010100101011
11011001001001100101	a	9
10011000010000101011	b	3
11110100011000011101	c	12
10110010110010111100	d	12

Table 5.4: Hamming distance for 20-bit codewords.

We were hoping to receive the 20-bit codeword for 'b', which is:
10011000010000101011
but we actually received:
100**0**100**1**010**1**00101011, where the error bits are highlighted.

Table 5.4 shows the Hamming distance calculation for this erroneous codeword measured against the four 20-bit codewords for the letters 'a' through to 'd'. As you can see, the minimum Hamming distance between the received codeword and the true letter codewords occurs with the letter 'b'. If our decoder used the minimum Hamming distance to select the correct letter, it would select 'b' since it is the nearest, with a Hamming distance of 3. Even though there were three errors in this received codeword, the correct letter was chosen. This is a significant improvement over **Table 5.2**, where a single bit error in the message results in the incorrect message being received.

You might argue that, increasing the message length would also increase the likelihood of more errors and that this technique would therefore not work. In fact, this was the view of the majority until 1948 when Claude Shannon completed his theoretical work to prove the benefits of an increased message length. There are some limitations, a key one being that this technique only works if the signal-to-noise level is above a certain limit: the *Shannon limit*. Above this limit, we can apply this technique of increasing the message length to reduce the received message error rate to an arbitrarily low level and, in theory, reduce the error rate to zero. Of course, in practice, this represents a target rather than a reality.

Although this seems counterintuitive, a simple explanation of how it works is possible. The key is the distance between the larger codewords, measured in our example by the Hamming distance. The larger this distance, the more unique each codeword is and the more it has to be distorted by errors to be confused with another codeword. In essence, we are averaging the errors over the longer codeword, rather than the shorter message and making use of the fact that the longer codewords are more distinct from each other.

Whilst Shannon's theory tells us that this will reduce the message error rate, it does not tell us how to select the larger codewords. In this example we used random 20-bit codewords and these were not optimised at all, but we could still see an advantage. The practical difficulty is that randomly-selected larger codewords are only possible in the simplest of cases. A 7-bit message has only 128 possible values but if the message was 75-bits long, then the number of possible messages would be $2^{75} > 10^{22}$, which is far too many to be searched for, even using modern computers. We need a method to code and decode these longer messages in real time to take advantage of this error correction technique.

Shannon's work in 1948 did not provide a method to determine how you could generate codewords from messages or vice versa, but others soon tackled the problem and today we have many methods available. These methods are based on a branch of mathematics called abstract algebra and are often named after mathematical concepts or the original inventors. Thus, we have convolution methods, Reed-Solomon codes (RS) and Low Density Parity Codes (LDPC), to name a few.

CONVOLUTION CODING

One of the earliest, and hence well studied, error coding techniques is convolution encoding. The term convolution refers to a mathematical technique, but we don't need the maths to have a basic understanding of the coding process.

Convolution coding can be applied to blocks of data, but it also works well with a data stream. The basic principle of convolution coding is similar to the CRC technique discussed, as it uses modulo-2 arithmetic but, unlike the CRC, it is best explained using a data stream rather than a block of data. It is illustrated in **Fig 5.7**.

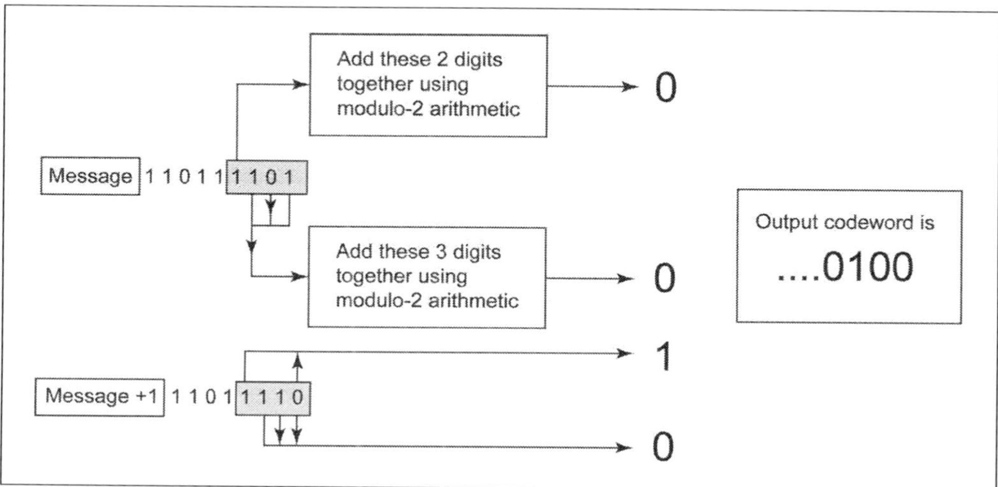

Fig 5.7: Convolution coding.

The message is shown on the left-hand side of the figure and consists of the data stream 110111101 which is passed through a 4-bit wide window. The values within this window are combined in specific ways, determined by what is called a polynomial and uses modulo-2 arithmetic similar to CRC, to produce two output values per bit in the message. In the figure, the message is advanced by only two bits but the output shown on the right consists of four values, thus we are doubling the number of bits in the coded message.

The width of the window, termed the code constraint length, is part of the convolution code's design as is the exact algorithms or polynomials to derive the two (or more) output parity bits that form the codeword.

Decoding the codewords is more complex than just applying the same algorithm at the receiver, since the actual message is not sent, just the output parity bits. The decoding is achieved using an algorithm first proposed by Andrew Viterbi in 1967 and hence the decoder is called a Viterbi decoder, and can be implemented in hardware or software.

Several of the WSJT modes make use of convolution coding and soft decision decoding, including JT4, JT9 and WSPR. They use a constraint length of 32 bits and produce two parity bits per message bit. The polynomials used to produce the output are given in the *WSJT User Guide* but, of course, to use the WSJT modes you do not need to consider these at all. Just use the software provided!

REED-SOLOMON ENCODING

As you might expect, convolution coding performance is not the most effective error coding technique although it is very widely used in current commercial digital communications. It also forms the basis of other, higher performance, encoding techniques called Turbo encoding. Another very commonly used error coding technique is Reed-Solomon (RS) encoding. It is widely used in data storage devices – hard drives, DVDs etc. It is also used in digital satellite TV – DVB. In amateur circles, it is used in the WSJT mode JT65.

RS encoding is a block encoding method which means it takes a block of data and encodes it by forming another longer block. RS codes are characterised by two numbers, n and k: k is the number of information bits to be encoded and n is the resulting number of bits in the encoded block. Thus in WSJT JT65, which uses RS(63,12), 12 information bits are encoded to become 63 bits. The JT65 message comprises 72 information bits and hence RS(63,12) encoding will produce a 6 x 63 = 378-bit coded message or codeword.

Since the mathematics of RS encoding ensure that each codeword is separated from the next valid codeword by the maximum Hamming distance, good error correction is achieved. An illustration of this difference is shown in **Fig 5.8.** Three messages are shown with a single character difference between them: G3LTF DL9KR JO40 and the two slightly different messages representing single differences or 'errors':

```
Message #1:   G3LTF DL9KR JO40
Packed message, 6-bit symbols:   61 37 30 28   9 27 61 58 26   3 49 16
Channel symbols, including FEC:
   14 16  9 18  4 60 41 18 22 63 43  5 30 13 15  9 25 35 50 21  0
   36 17 42 33 35 39 22 25 39 46  3 47 39 55 23 61 25 58 47 16 38
   39 17  2 36  4 56  5 16 15 55 18 41  7 26 51 17 18 49 10 13 24

Message #2:   G3LTE DL9KR JO40
Packed message, 6-bit symbols:   61 37 30 28   5 27 61 58 26   3 49 16
Channel symbols, including FEC:
   20 34 19  5 36  6 30 15 22 20  3 62 57 59 19 56 17 35  2  9 41
   10 23 24 41 35 39 60 48 33 34 49 54 53 55 23 24 59  7  9 39 51
   23 17  2 12 49  6 46  7 61 49 18 41 50 16 40  8 45 55 45  7 24

Message #3:   G3LTF DL9KR JO41
Packed message, 6-bit symbols:   61 37 30 28   9 27 61 58 26   3 49 17
Channel symbols, including FEC:
   47 27 46 50 58 26 38 24 22  3 14 54 10 58 36 23 63 35 41 56 53
   62 11 49 14 35 39 60 40 44 15 45  7 44 55 23 12 49 39 11 18 36
   26 17  2  8 60 44 37  5 48 44 18 41 32 63  4 49 55 57 37 13 25
```

Fig 5.8: JT65 message encoded using RS(63,12) (Taylor, 2005).

G3LT**E** DL9KR JO40 and G3LTF DL9KR JO4**1**

Each message is shown in digital form by the row of numbers beginning with 61 37... It would have been better to show the true binary codes here but that would have made the figure very difficult to analyse so the binary numbers have been compressed into 6-bit values and written in decimal: the sequence 61 37 is really 111101 011111. These 6-bit values are termed symbols in the figure and we will meet this term later on when we discuss modulation methods.

Notice that the three messages are very similar and in binary only differ by the fifth symbol or the last symbol corresponding to the position of the 'error' differences.

Now look at the three encoded messages – they are completely different. This shows the advantage of using FEC encoding because these encoded messages are much easier to distinguish between, even on a noisy radio channel.

Reed-Solomon encoding occurs at the symbol level so the encoder will take the 12-symbol message – 61 37 30 28 9 27 61 58 26 3 49 16 and encode it to make the 63 symbols to be sent over the channel. RS(63,12) is capable of correcting up to 25 symbol errors in the 63 symbol codeword. Its performance correcting burst errors is thus excellent.

LOW DENSITY PARITY CHECK ENCODING

In a search for encoding techniques that approach the Shannon limit, *low density parity check* (LDPC) encoding has been shown to be one of the best techniques and represents the current state of the art in FEC. Although they were discovered in the early 1960s their complexity and the lack of computing power at that time meant that they were ignored for more than 20 years. Although rediscovered in the 1980s they were not really developed any further until the 1990s. As computing power increased, this encoding technique has become more practical.

Today LDPC encoding is seen as a potential FEC encoding technique in 5G mobile telephone networks as well as next generation wi-fi. In amateur circles, FT8 uses LDPC FEC encoding combined with a CRC.

SYNCHRONISATION

So far we have produced our message, encoded it using an efficient source coding technique, added an error checking code, such as a CRC, and finally expanded the message length using an FEC technique. There is one more thing to do before we can modulate an RF carrier and transmit the message over a radio channel: we need to tell the receiver when the message starts.

A common way of doing this is by using start and stop bits as was discussed in a previous section. This system has been in use by RTTY systems for over 50 years. To improve on this, PSK31 uses a varicode alphabet that has been designed to exclude the bit combination 00 – there are no characters in this varicode that contain the sequence 00. Synchronisation is then achieved by sending 00 between characters.

If the digital message is sent as a block message, an alternative is to use a fixed synchronisation pattern that is added to the actual message before it is sent that will allow the receiver to synchronise with the transmitter. For example, JT65 interleaves a pseudo-random synchronisation pattern with the message. Synchronisation is so important that half of the final message is devoted to this sequence. FT8 uses three patterns, termed Costas arrays, one at the beginning, one in the middle and one at the end of each message block.

In highly structured messages, such as those produced by the WSJT modes, UTC (coordinated universal time) is used to allow the receiver to synchronise to the whole message sequence. It is for this reason that an accurate UTC clock is needed. However, this is not accurate enough to determine the exact message start, so some form of bit or symbol synchronisation method is still needed.

MODULATION METHODS I – ANALOGUE

We are all familiar with the basic modulation types that have been in use by amateur stations for many years: amplitude modulation (AM), single sideband (SSB), frequency modulation (FM) and, of course, CW. Digital modes use these and even more exotic types, but the most important modulation type for HF digital modes is frequency shift keying (FSK) and phase shift keying (PSK).

Before we discuss these in detail, let us backtrack to AM and SSB. In AM the radio carrier is amplitude modulated by the audio signal which is usually speech.

Fig 5.9 shows this can be represented in two different ways: in terms of frequency or in terms of time. Typically an AM signal occupies twice the audio bandwidth of an SSB signal, having both upper (USB) and lower (LSB) sidebands centred on the radio carrier frequency. AM is quite easy to generate and can be received even on a crystal set. It was very common in the early days of radio, including amateur radio. Commercially, it is still used today on the long, medium and short-wave broadcast bands and it remains an option on most current HF amateur transceivers.

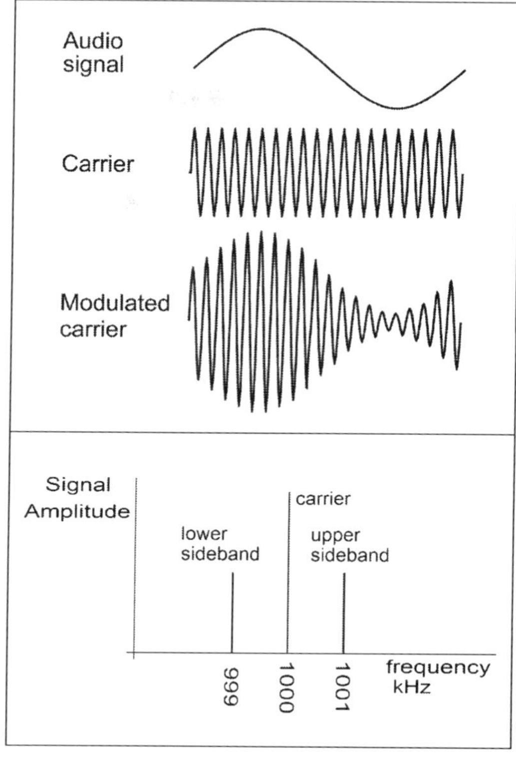

Fig 5.9: Amplitude modulation.

For working DX using speech, AM has been replaced by SSB because this modulation technique is more efficient. This is because it puts all of the RF energy into the information-carrying sideband and it has a smaller spectrum requirement, **Fig 5.10**.

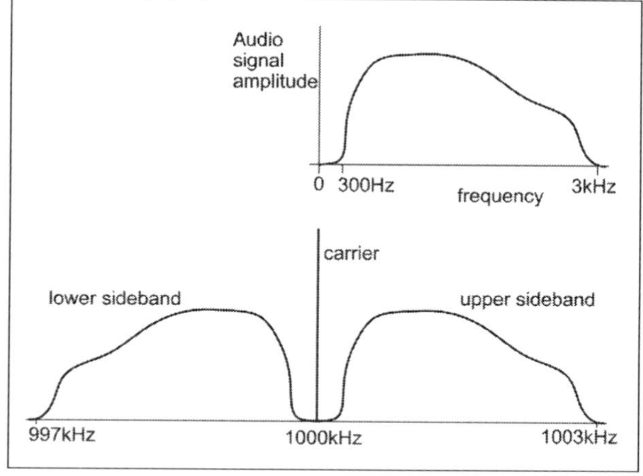

Fig 5.10: Single sideband modulation.

There are several methods of creating SSB but the classical method is by filtering an AM signal in the IF stages to remove one sideband and the carrier. In a transceiver, this filtering is shared by both transmit and receive functions. Typically, this is a 2.7kHz bandwidth crystal filter that defines the IF bandwidth. On modern transceivers, this filtering is often achieved using DSP techniques, which also offer the advantage of a user-definable variable bandwidth.

Finally, we have what is often described as the most efficient modulation type: CW. Here of course, we switch the RF carrier on and off using a Morse key to generate Morse code. It uses a very narrow spectrum, less than that used by SSB and is preferred by many as the 'ultimate' DX mode. It could also be described as the first digital mode, since it is binary: on or off. Even CW occupies a finite bandwidth due to the keying rate. Any abrupt transitions in the waveform due to keying will also extend the bandwidth and it is for this reason that some form of filtering is used to avoid these key clicks. In modern transceivers this is often adjustable using the menu system.

Since the early days of radio communications, it was noticed that the narrower the receiver bandwidth, the less noise was received, so this gave narrow modes an advantage when working DX. Hence, CW was deemed more noise efficient then SSB, while SSB was better than AM. Another factor was the power efficiency of each mode. In AM the transmitted power is split into three, the carrier and two sidebands, but the information (that is, the speech) is only in the sidebands and they are mirrors of each other. Thus SSB, which transmits only one sideband containing all the information, is much more power efficient than AM. CW also has this power efficiency advantage over AM.

Despite these advantages, all three of these modulation methods suffer from the effects of noise. Any received noise is added to the signal and, if sufficiently large, will swamp the signal and make recovering the information impossible. For this reason, the signal-to-noise ratio is an important measure of the quality of the radio channel. At the threshold where the noise makes the recovery of the information impossible, it becomes a measure of the modulation efficiency.

In amateur radio circles, the signal-to-noise ratio is usually defined in a 2.5kHz bandwidth as:

$$SNR = \frac{average\ signal\ power}{average\ noise\ power\ in\ 2.5kHz}$$

It is usually expressed in dB rather than as a fraction:

$$SNR_{dB} = log_{10}(SNR)$$

As an example, it has been suggested that to resolve SSB requires a SNR of +10dB whereas CW can be resolved down to an SNR of –18dB **(http://www.pa3fwm.nl/technotes/tn09b.html)**. These figures are of course approximate and should only be taken as indicative of the difference between CW and SSB.

Before moving on to the modulation methods used in digital transmissions, we should briefly discuss another common modulation method: frequency modulation (FM). AM, SSB and CW are all amplitude modulation methods but we can also modulate the RF carrier's frequency rather than its amplitude. This is shown in **Fig 5.11**.

The frequency spectrum of an FM carrier has more sidebands than an AM carrier and hence the bandwidth requirement is larger. It is for this reason that most FM channels are found in the VHF and above frequency bands. Commercial FM stations can occupy 75kHz but amateur usage it is often limited to 5kHz.

The advantage of FM is its higher noise immunity due to being less susceptible to additive noise. This is because FM receivers only respond to frequency variations and not the amplitude variations associated with most radio noise. For this reason, a commercial FM station can have up to 20dB signal-to-noise advantage over an equivalent AM station: **http://www.commsp.ee.ic.ac.uk/~kkleung/Communications2_2009/Lecture5.pdf**

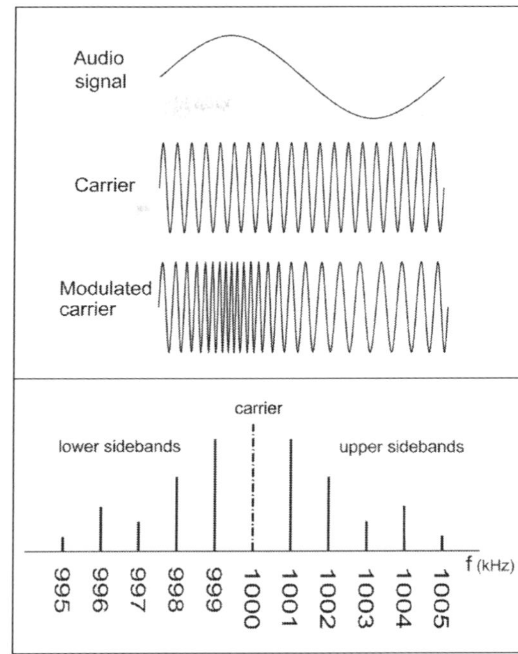

Fig 5.11: FM modulation.

MODULATION METHODS II – DIGITAL

Digital modulation methods are an extension of the above modulation methods. As we discussed in the previous section, digital information is encoded into bits and bytes, so the modulation methods need to encode these bits and bytes on to an RF carrier in a similar manner to the way in which speech modulation methods encode speech on to an RF carrier. The analogue modulation method that is similar to binary data is CW.

Fig 5.12 shows a carrier wave being switched on and off according to a binary signal. Apart from the switching speed, each binary 1 represented by the

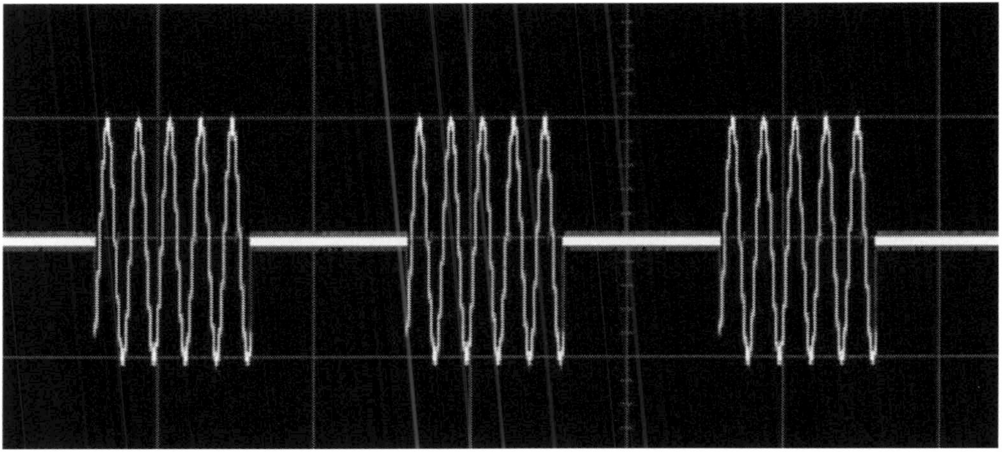

Fig 5.12: Amplitude Shift Keying.

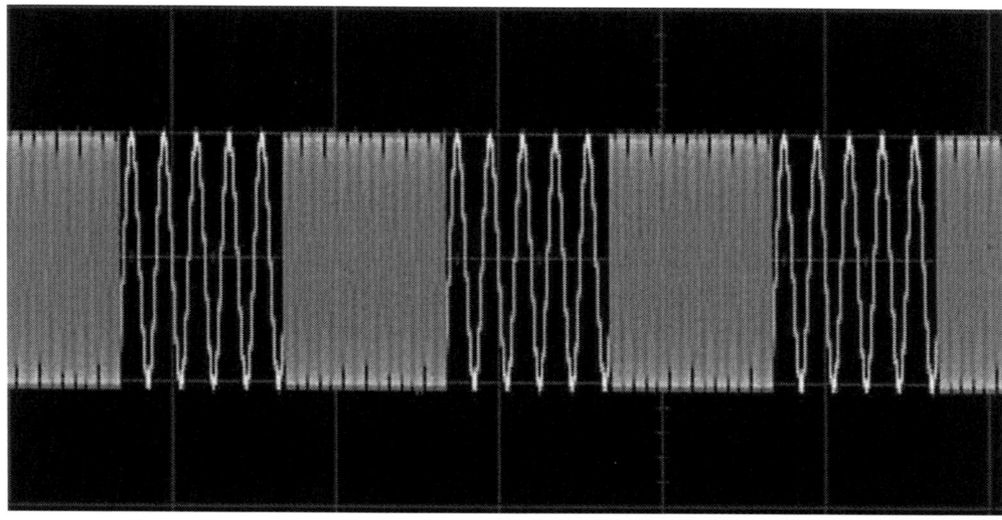

Fig 5.13: Frequency Shift Keying.

carrier wave only contains a few cycles of the RF, this could be a Morse letter S albeit with horrendous keying harmonics due to the rapid switching. This form of modulation is called Amplitude Shift Keying (ASK). It suffers from the same susceptibility to noise as a Morse CW signal and, since digital transmission requires a low error rate, it is not used in practice except when combined with other modulation modes.

Following on from our discussion of the noise advantages of FM, we can consider the modulation mode shown in **Fig 5.13**. Here the binary information is modulated on to a carrier by shifting the carrier frequency between two frequencies, one representing a binary 1 and the other a binary 0, hence the name binary FSK or BFSK. **Fig 5.13** shows a simple 1010101 binary pattern modulation using two distinct frequencies. FSK, like FM, is less susceptible to noise than ASK. It is often the frequency shift that is specified rather than exact frequencies, for example, amateur Radioteletype (RTTY) is one of the oldest digital systems and it uses a frequency shift of 170Hz with the lower frequency representing a binary 1 and the upper frequency a binary 0. Other variants of RTTY exist that use alternative frequency shifts, but the 170Hz shift is the most common.

It is not necessary to just use two frequencies for FSK; it is perfectly possible to use more frequencies and **Fig 5.14** shows a scheme using four frequencies. However, the relationship to binary 1s and 0s then becomes slightly more complex now that we have four possible states. A simple encoding relates each frequency to not one binary digit (1 or 0) but to a sequence of two, for example, if the frequencies are F1, F2, F3 and F4 we could set F1=00, F2=01, F3=10 and F4=11. Now we have the added complexity of encoding a binary number,

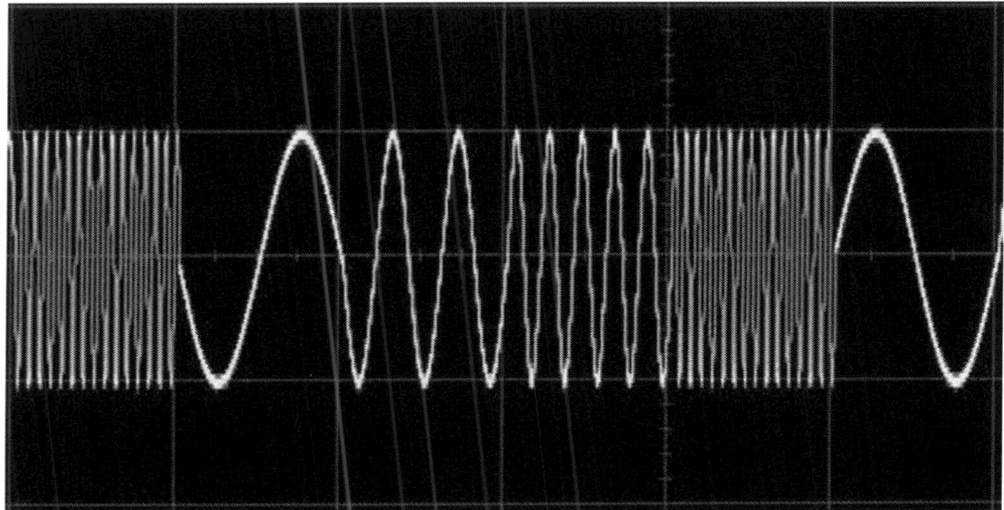

Fig 5.14: 4-FSK uses four different frequencies.

say 10011100, as a series of frequencies which in this case would be 10=F3, 01=F2, 11=F4 and 00=F1, so the sequence is F3 F2 F4 F1. To distinguish between binary (0 and 1) modulation and this, more complex, form we refer to the modulation elements as symbols, rather than binary digits. To make this notation consistent, we can define a modulation index that relates the size of binary number sent to the number of symbols in the modulation scheme.

$$Number\ of\ symbols = 2^m$$

where m equals the number of information bits sent in each symbol. Thus in our example of 4-FSK the number of symbols (frequencies) is 4 and hence m = 2. Each symbol represents a two-digit binary number. For example, FT8 uses 8-FSK and hence m = 3 for this mode: each symbol represents a 3-bit binary number. It is worth noting that, when each symbol represents more than one bit, there is a difference between the rate of transmission measured in bits/second and the rate of symbols transmitted. For example, if we are using FSK switching between two frequencies, as in RTTY, each symbol represents just 1 bit and the bit rate is the same as the symbol rate, but if we are using 8-FSK each symbol represents 3 bits, so the bit rate will be three times the symbol rate.

The symbol rate is called the *baud rate*. Whilst some form of FSK is used in the majority of the WSJT digital modes, there is another modulation method that is commonly used in amateur HF digital: *Phase Shift Keying* (PSK). **Fig 5.15** shows a binary PSK waveform (BPSK). Here the frequency of the carrier is not changed but the transition between a binary 1 and 0 is indicated by a 180º instantaneous phase change in the carrier. This is seen as the 'W' in the other-

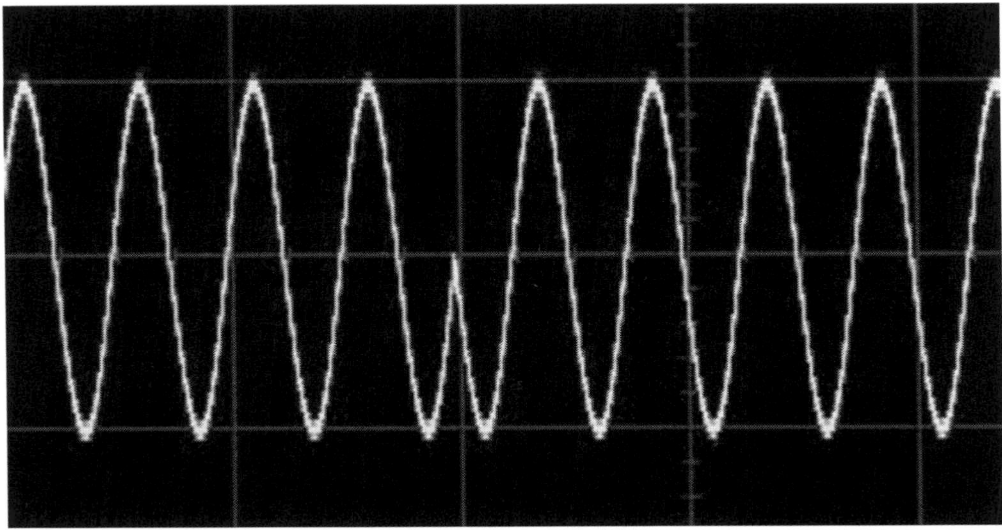

Fig 5.15: Phase Shift Keying.

wise regular carrier sine wave. This can be generated in hardware by switching between two oscillators which are 180º in phase apart or, more often today, by software using direct frequency synthesis within a PC sound card. In practice, such abrupt phase transitions will cause the signal bandwidth to be huge and some form of filtering is used in the same way as we remove key clicks in CW transmissions. In software this is done by smoothing the phase transition by imposing an envelope defined by a mathematical function: often a raised cosine curve.

Demodulating BPSK requires an accurate measurement of the phase and which phase represents a binary 1 and a binary 0. This requires a very accurate receiver local oscillator and as such is not commonly used in amateur communications. One method to avoid this stringent requirement placed upon the receive local oscillator is to use differential BPSK (DBPSK). In this method the phase shift is with reference to the previous bit so that a series of 1s or 0s will not have any phase changes between each bit. There is only a phase change when there is a change from 0 to 1 or vice versa. DBPSK is used in the PSK31 HF digital mode developed by Peter Martinez, G3PLX, in the 1990s. PSK31 is a high-performance mode that generally outperforms RTTY.

Just as with FSK, PSK is not limited to a single-phase transition of 180º and multiple phase transitions are possible. Quadrature PSK (QPSK) uses four phases to encode the binary information and this is used in QPSK31, a variant of PSK31. A similar modulation method called offset QPSK (OQPSK) is used in the WSJT mode MSK144 which is aimed at amateur meteor-scatter communications.

Just as we defined an SNR for analogue modulation, we can define an SNR applicable to digital modulation techniques. We replace the average signal power with the energy per bit, E_b, and the average noise in 2.5kHz by the noise power in 1Hz bandwidth, N_0.

$$SNR = \frac{E_b}{N_0}$$

This is the preferred measurement of signal-to-noise ratio in the professional world and is used to measure the relative performance of digital systems. However, in the amateur world, we prefer the definition used previously for analogue signals, so the SNR provided by software packages such as WSJT-X uses this earlier definition:

$$SNR_{db} = \log_{10} \frac{average\ signal\ power}{average\ noise\ power\ in\ 2.5kHz}$$

GENERATING DIGITAL MODES

Although these digital modulation methods seem complex, they can be generated quite easily using an SSB transceiver and a PC sound card. The sound card can be programmed to produce any audio waveform using the direct synthesis method, where a series of numbers representing the amplitude of the waveform are sent to a DAC. FSK is achieved by creating a sequence of audio tones generated by the sound card and inputting these to an appropriate audio input on the transceiver. Sometimes this method of modulation is termed Audio Frequency Shift Keying (AFSK) but the result, when applied to an SSB transmitter, is identical to FSK.

If we input a pure audio tone at, say, 1kHz into a transceiver set to USB and tuned to 14.000MHz, the RF output will be on 14.001MHz. If we change the audio tone to 2kHz, the output changes to 14.002MHz. When sending an FT8 message we would be switching between eight tones whereas with JT65 it would be 65 different tones. It is this characteristic that gives each mode its recognisable warbling sound.

Generating, switching and streaming tones from the sound card is achieved in software using a specialist *application programming interface* (API) and although it requires quite intricate programming, it is no more difficult than any other programming activity. Of course, if you just want to use these modulation modes, you do not need to program at all but just use the freely-available software packages. However, if you want to delve deeper into the technology and understand how the software does what it does, you will eventually meet APIs.

THE RADIO CHANNEL

Radio channels are characterised by noise level, multi-path propagation, which causes fading and timing issues and Doppler shift due to movement somewhere in the path. These characteristics are generally random, although some can be expected to be present, their overall property is a lack of predictability.

Noise is present in all radio channels and it limits the ultimate communication performance of the channel. We usually distinguish between naturally-occurring noise and man-made noise but the effects on performance are similar. What is more important are the properties of the noise. The basic noise floor is seen as a random fluctuation in received amplitude and has the characteristic of being relatively frequency independent. Hence it is termed broadband or *white noise* and represented by N_0, the noise power spectrum density, used in the calculation of the signal-to-noise ratio. In addition to this white noise, there are bursts of noise due to thunderstorms and, of course, man-made sources such as car ignition systems. The lower HF bands are very susceptible to lightning-induced noise bursts, especially at night, whereas the higher HF and VHF bands are affected by ignition noise. Power lines also produce a characteristic noise that adds to the overall noise present in the channel.

Multi-path reception occurs when there is more than one propagation path open in the channel. Various combinations of ground wave, single-hop sky wave, line of sight, refraction and reflection can be present at the same time to make multiple paths. Different paths will have different path lengths and, consequently, there will be timing and phase differences between the signals arriving at the reception point. This gives rise to interference between the signals, causing fading and the different arrival times cause synchronisation problems for digital signals.

Doppler effects are due to relative motion between parts of the signal path. This could be due to movement of the source or the receiver relative to one another or reflections from a moving reflector, the moon, a meteorite or a satellite, for example. It is not just the frequency that is shifted, the Doppler effect can also shift the phase of a signal. This can be very important for PSK-modulated signals.

These characteristics of the radio channel form part of the design parameters for the overall communication system. In analogue systems we rely on reducing the receiver bandwidth to reduce the noise and the human brain to decipher the signal as it fades in and out or is blocked by a noise burst. However, in digital systems we must design them to be as tolerant to the radio channel as possible. It is here that coding techniques such as FEC and the modulation type and rate of communication are all decided. For example, JT65 was originally designed for use in moonbounce communications, so it used a 46-second transmission period, a low communication rate of 2.7 baud, MFSK modulation that is tolerant to Doppler effects and a strong Reed-Solomon FEC. Moonbounce is a slow communications channel. This can be compared to MSK144 designed for meteor scatter communications that uses a 72ms transmission period, a high communications rate of 2000 baud, OQPSK modulation and strong LDPC FEC. Clearly MSK144 is aimed at a fast-changing radio channel.

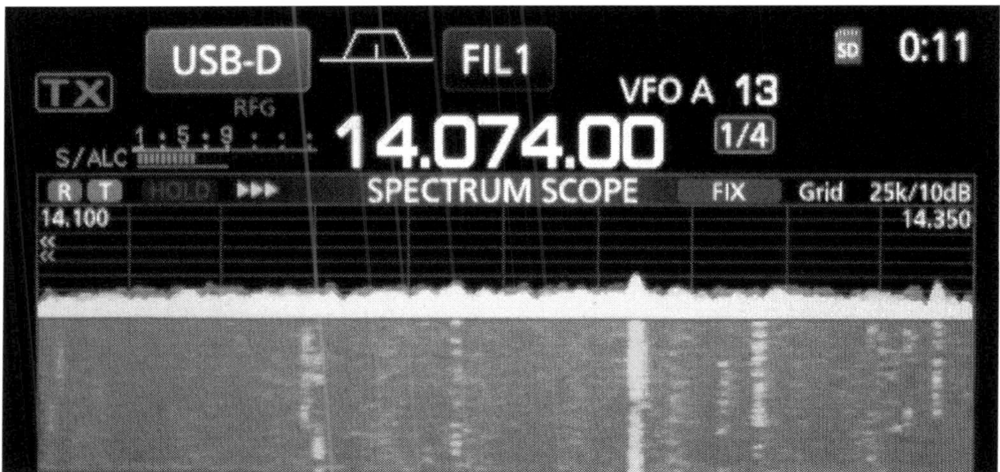

Fig 5.16: Icom IC-7300 waterfall display.

DEMODULATING THE RECEIVED SIGNAL

Tuning-in to a CW or SSB transmission takes some care but with practice it becomes straightforward. Demodulating digital signals, on the other hand, used to require careful tuning to the exact frequency of the transmission before the decoder could operate. One of the many benefits of changing to computer-based demodulation of digital modes is the ability to demodulate and decode several digital signals at the same time. The waterfall display is now ubiquitous when using digital modes software, but how does it work?

Understanding the display is easy, since it is just a visual representation of what is being received, with frequency across the bottom and time on the vertical axis. As you watch the display, it 'falls' down the screen, recording the way in which the signals develop with time. It is a spectrum analyser that covers the 3kHz or so of the audio from the receiver. Until not so long ago, computing this in real time was not possible, but with the increasing power of computers it has become available even on an average PC. In fact, many modern transceivers such as the Icom IC-7300, **Fig 5.16**, incorporate waterfall displays as part of their main frequency displays. The technology behind the waterfall is *Fourier analysis*.

FOURIER ANALYSIS

Fourier analysis is generally accepted as an advanced mathematical technique that requires a strong mathematical background well beyond what the average radio amateur has achieved. However, the general concept is quite straightforward; it is a technique that calculates the frequency spectrum from an amplitude-time waveform. The frequency spectrum is a familiar concept to most radio amateurs since we often talk about filters, the bandwidth of signals and sidebands.

Fig 5.17 shows a typical frequency spectrum of amplitude versus frequency. It does not seem an easy task to convert the amplitude - time waveform to this spectrum; however, consider the opposite conversion. Can we convert a frequency spectrum to a waveform? Now all we need to do is to add up a series of time waveforms each corresponding to a specific frequency. **Fig 5.18** shows this

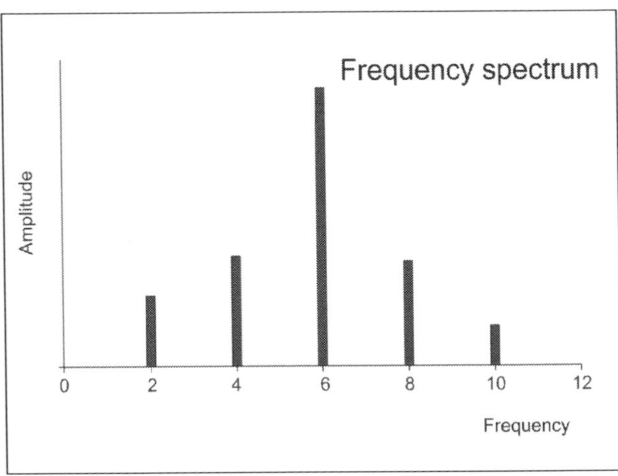

Fig 5.17: Typical frequency spectrum.

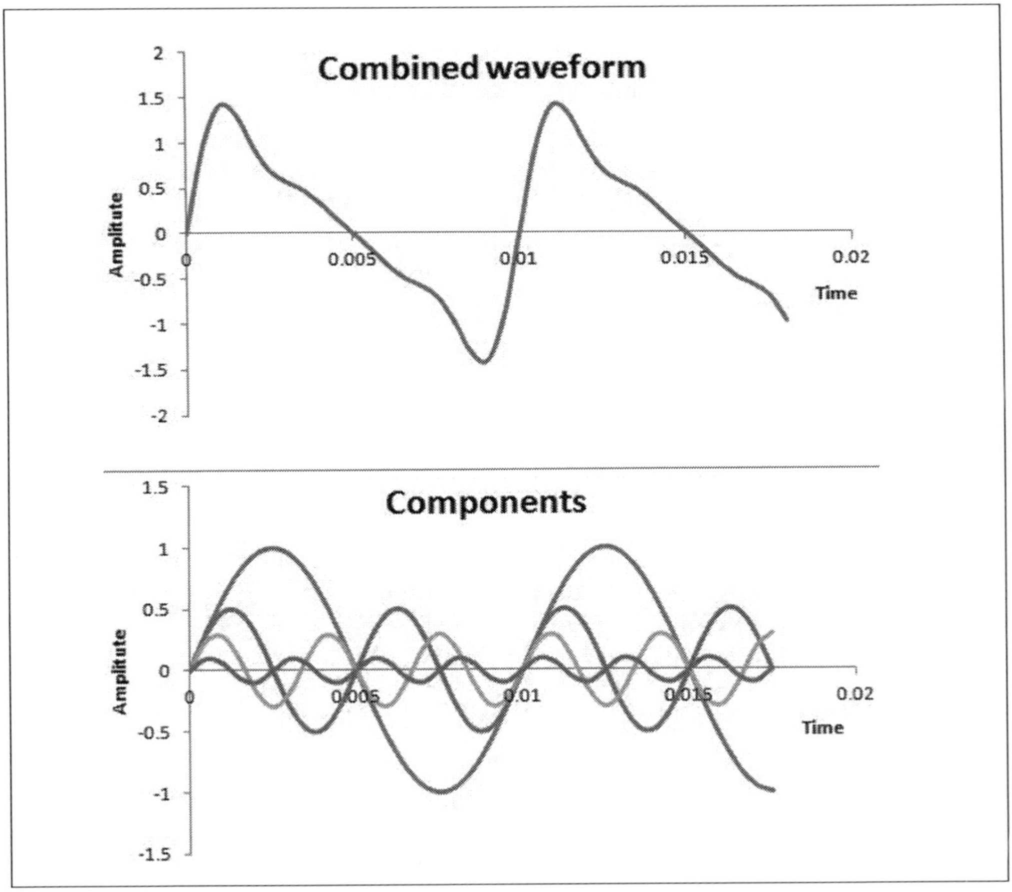

Fig 5.18: Combining frequencies.

process. Four waveforms of different frequencies are combined to make the top waveform. In this example, the frequencies are 100Hz, 200Hz, 300Hz and 400Hz and differing 'amounts' of each of these harmonics are added. This addition is point-wise; that is to say each point on the four waveforms at a single time are added together to make the combined waveform. Notice that the combined waveform is not a pure sine wave but looks more like a saw tooth waveform.

The insight that Fourier had was that any amplitude - time waveform can be constructed in this manner from a series of pure sine waves whose frequencies are harmonically related. Of course, it often takes many, many pure sine waves to make any specific waveform. There is an assumption here that the combined waveform is repetitive – the shape of the waveform is repeated over and over again. **Fig 5.18** shows the repeating part of the waveform between 0 and 0.01 seconds.

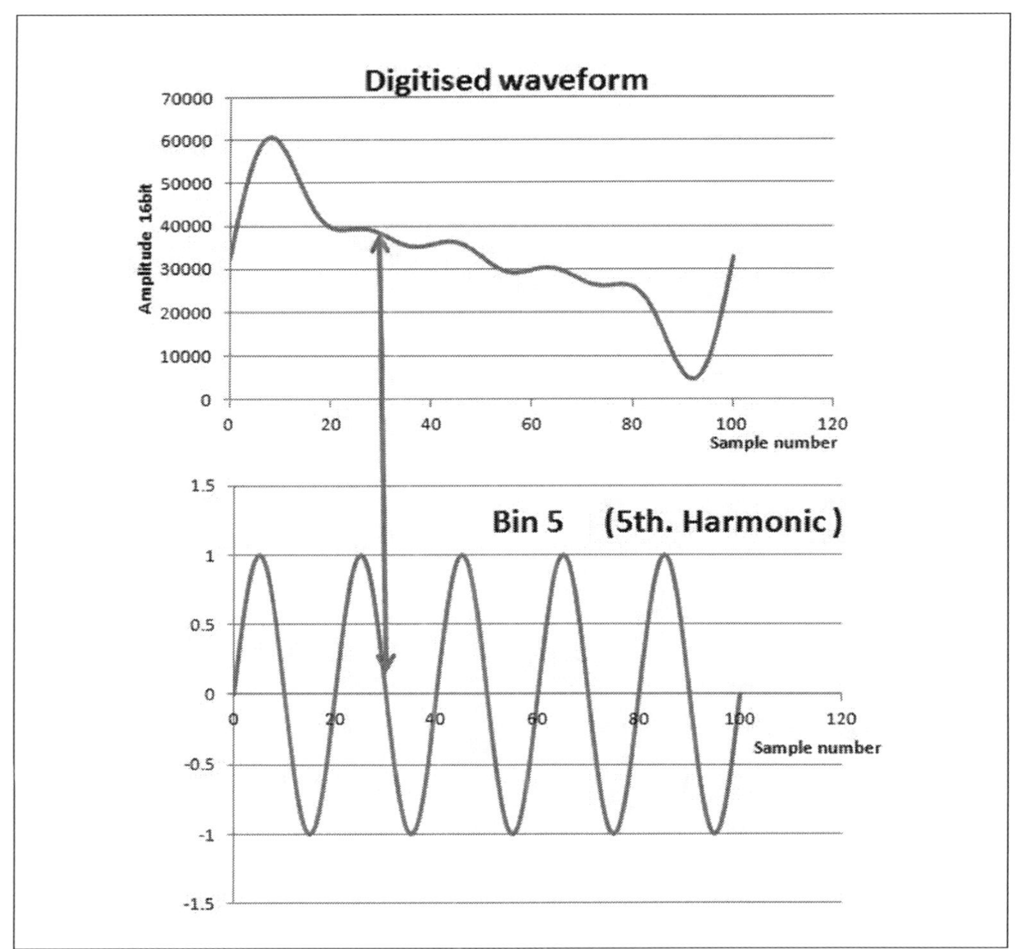

Fig 5.19: FFT of a waveform produces 5th harmonic.

When the waveforms are in digital / sampled form this combination process is straightforward. If each waveform is sampled in the same way you just need to add the binary values, something that is easy in software.

The reverse of this process begins by determining the periodicity of the input waveform. In practice this is usually achieved by mere selection: choosing to select 1024, 2048 or 4096 points from the waveform's digital stream and then repeating this process. There is a computational efficiency if you choose a power of 2, but this is beyond our present discussion. If we have a 48k sample / second data stream, then 4096 samples equates to approximately 85ms or 12Hz. Although choosing the number of points does determine the real temporal periodicity measured in seconds, time is usually measured in points rather than in seconds.

Fig 5.19 shows the digitised waveform to be analysed at the top. At the bottom is a pure sine wave that is a harmonic of the periodicity. Each harmonic is termed a *bin* and **Fig 5.19** shows the calculation of the amplitude in bin 5. Each point in the digitised waveform is multiplied by the corresponding point in the lower pure sine wave and summed and averaged by dividing the sum by the number of points. In the case of **Fig 5.19** this is a 100-point waveform, so we divide by 100.

The amplitudes for the first 7 bins are plotted in **Fig 5.20**. Bin 1 corresponds to a frequency of 100Hz, bin 2 to 200Hz and so forth. If we have a 48k sample / second data stream, 4096 samples equates to approximately 85ms or 12Hz so the FFT will provide a spectrum in multiples of this frequency: 12Hz, 24Hz, 36Hz and so forth.

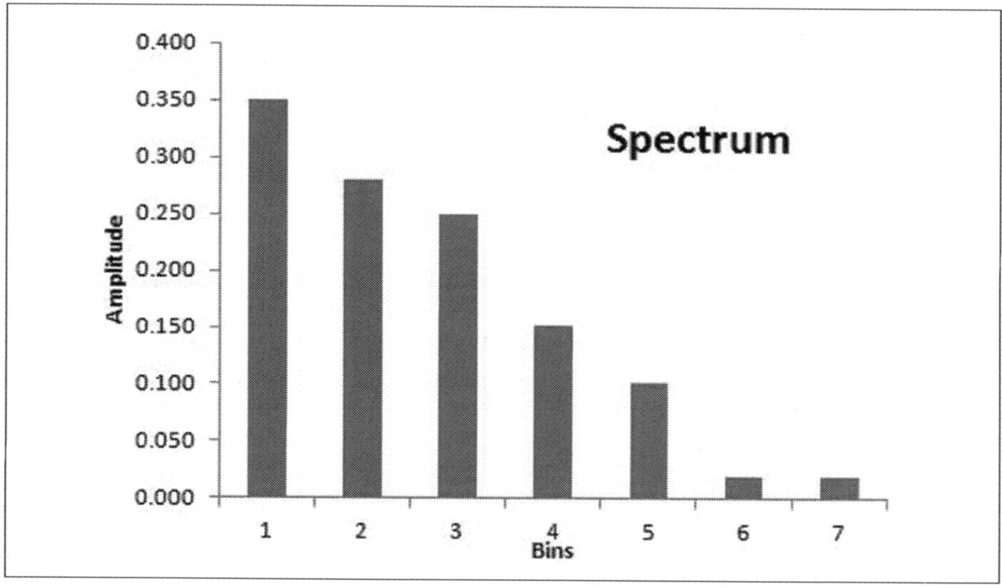

Fig 5.20: Amplitude of the first 7 FFT spectrum bins.

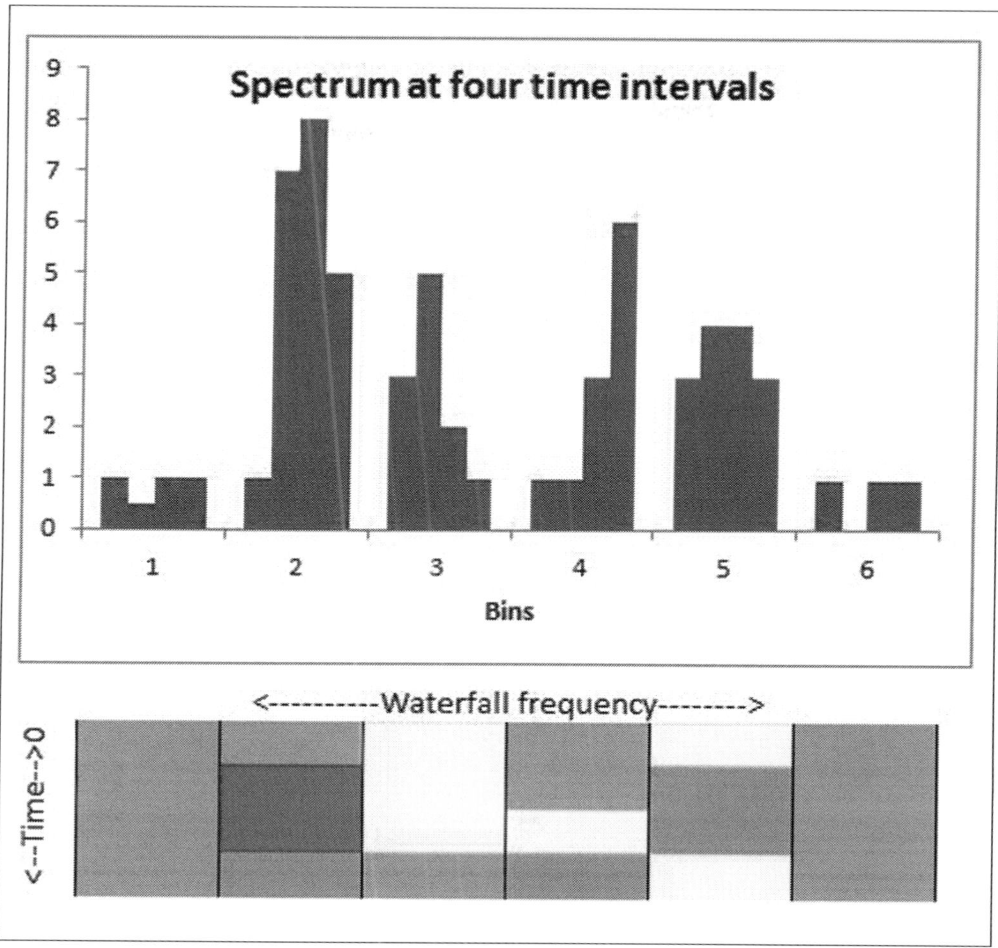

Fig 5.21: FFT and the waterfall.

In practice, the FFT calculation is repeated over and over to produce a moving spectrogram or waterfall display. This shows how the spectrum changes over time, as illustrated in **Fig 5.21**.

The FFT is calculated four times and each bin has four levels corresponding to the value calculated for the bin at four consecutive times. These are then transferred to a moving waterfall display where each value is assigned a colour. Each colour is assigned to a range of values. The waterfall display is a key part of the tuning process in digital modes.

FSK is simple to demodulate in this way since the separate frequencies transmitted will fall in different frequency bins. It is then possible for the software to search the whole audio bandwidth and search out the FSK signals. Hence software such as WSJT-X, JTDX and MSHV can decode several digital QSOs at the same time and provide the operator with a list of stations that are operating.

PSK is slightly harder to demodulate and requires the receiver to synchronise with the carrier signal. However, the waterfall can be of use to select the signal from the ones that are available.

SOURCE DECODING

Source decoding poses few issues since the encoding process can simply be reversed to create the original message

SUMMARY

In this chapter we have covered the technology behind digital modes. Having first broken down a generic digital transmission system into its component parts, we then explored each part in depth. Particular attention was paid to the importance of error control and modulation methods and how these combine in a well-designed system, to give the outstanding weak-signal performance. Finally, we explained, using diagrams, Fourier analysis and the FFT, a mathematical technique that has revolutionised how we make use of digital modes.

Index

Always the best Amateur Radio books

radiotoday
Guide to the Yaesu FTDX10

By Andrew Barron, ZL3DW

The Yaesu FTDX10 is much more than just a cut down version of the Yaesu FTDX101 as some might think. Andrew Barron, ZL3DW brings you the practical guide to getting the most out these highly rated transceivers.

In common with all the other books in this Radio Today series the *radiotoday guide to the Yaesu FTDX10* provides a practical and easy to understand guide to these great radios. This is not simply a 'rehash' of the Yaesu User Manual, nor does it try to replace it. Andrew for example explains not just what the control does, but also how and when to use it. The FTdx10 employs the same cutting edge 'Hybrid SDR' (software defined radio) receiver architecture as the FTDX101 and Andrew explains how to get the most from it. You are also offered tips on how the author set up his FTdx10 and his 'real world' experiences.

If you own a Yaesu FTdx10 or are just interested in how they work before buying one the *radiotoday guide to the Yaesu FTDX10* provides a highly illuminating guide.

Size 176x240mm, 208 Pages
ISBN: 9781913995157
ONLY £15.99

radiotoday
Guide to the Yaesu FTDX101

By Andrew Barron, ZL3DW

The Yaesu FTdx101D and FTdx101MP transceivers are superb and highly rated radios but, if you own one or are considering buying one, are you aware of all the useful features and how achieve the full potential it offers? This is where the *radiotoday guide to the Yaesu FTdx101* comes in. This book provides a practical and easy to understand guide to these great radios.

The radiotoday guide to the Yaesu FTdx101 does not simply duplicate the manuals that describe each button function, and control but is a 'how to do it' book. From the front panel that is dominated by the full-colour 7" touchscreen display to the VFO tuning knob, the book describes the use of the 'proper' buttons and knobs alongside setting the myriad of touchscreen controls.

The *radiotoday guide to the Yaesu FTdx101* provides an easily understood insight into the setup and operation of these great radios that every owner or potential buyer will find invaluable.

Size 176x240mm, 208 Pages
ISBN: 9781913995102
ONLY £15.99

RSGB BOOKSHOP

Always the best Amateur Radio books

Computers in Amateur Radio

3rd Edition

Edited by Lorna Smart, 2E0POI

Amateur Radio is a fast-moving technological world with much done in conjunction with equally fast-moving world of computers. Amateur radio interacts far beyond traditional personal computers with much use made of Raspberry Pi computers, mobile phones and other technologies. *Computers in Amateur Radio* provides a practical guide to what is out there for those who wish to discover the areas where the two technologies combine.

This newly revised and updated edition of *Computers in Amateur Radio* expands on the evolving world of computers and that has developed since the previous edition as well as introducing readers to newer technologies and methods. There are eighteen chapters covering a wide array of topics for Radio Amateurs. You will find coverage of Data Modes, antenna modelling, propagation modelling. Software Defined Radios, the Raspberry Pi, mobile phones to name a few.

Computers in Amateur Radio is a must have companion book for both those who are new to the hobby and the more experienced user. It works well both as a manual and a reference guide with its many illustrated step-by-step guides and reference information. Readers will find *Computers in Amateur Radio* has something of interest and value for everyone wishing to explore or develop their use of computers in Amateur Radio.

Size 174x240mm, 192pages

ISBN: 9781913995287

ONLY £15.99

www.rsgbshop.org

on orders over £30. See T&Cs

Radio Society of Great Britain, 3 Abbey Court, Priory Business Park, Bedford, MK44 3WH Tel: 01234 8327